THE

MARINE ELECTRICS BOOK

REPAIR AND MAINTENANCE

Geoffrey O'Connell

Published by Ashford, Buchan & Enright, Leatherhead, Surrey.

Author © Geoffrey O'Connell 1991
Illustrations© Geoffrey O'Connell 1991
Packaged by Willowbridge Publishing, Bletchley, Milton Keynes, Bucks.
Printed & bound by: Hartnolls, Bodmin, Cornwall, England.

British Library Cataloguing in Publication Data

O'Connell, Geoffrey
The marine electrics book
I. Title
623.8503

ISBN 1-85253-210-6

Errors and omissions

Whilst great care has been taken in the compilation of this book, it is regretted that neither author nor publisher can accept responsibility for the use, or consequences of the use of the information and opinions expressed herein, nor for any inaccuracies or mishaps arising from the work.

Disclaimer

The author has no commercial connection with any business or firm listed herein, other than as a partner of Willowbridge Enterprises, and no warranty or guarantee is implied or given in their respect.

That a business, firm, or product is not listed, or detailed, does not imply any criticism. The impressions, opinions and viewpoints expressed in this publication are highly individualistic and readers must make their own judgements on all the matter presented herein.

Illustrations by G.R. O'Connell, Paul Sumpner & Ted Spittles
Photographs by G.R. O'Connell & Ted Spittles
Cover design by Flemons & Lockwood, Havant, Hants.

ACKNOWLEDGEMENTS

If I was listing my grateful thanks, in chronological order, then Bob Bingham of South Western Marine Factors would still have to be first named. Years ago now, Bob set me off on the trials and tribulations of authorship by commissioning the progenitor of a companion book in this series. He has much for which to answer!

As indicated in the introduction, Paul Sumpner was responsible for much of the original 'basic building blocks' of each Chapter, from which the book has grown and developed. Viv Hitie pounded the word processor, whilst Ted Spittles performed a magnificent job of crafting the original sketches into the final technical drawings and illustrations.

A number of manufacturers and firms, associated with the marine industry, were helpful in my preparation of the book, some far beyond the call of duty. The most co-operative included Stowe Marine Equipment Ltd, Taplins Marine, South Western Marine Factors, Nautech Ltd and Navstar Ltd. Their full title and respective addresses, as well as those of other companies who will be useful to the reader, and who may have supplied information, are to be found in Chapter 12.

As spelt out in the text, I have no commercial connection with any firm detailed in the book, other than as a partner of a small, Inland Waterways boatyard.

**About
The Author**

Geoffrey O'Connell has a very wide experience of all aspects of boat building and marine engineering, spanning some thirty-two years. A Mechanical Engineering apprenticeship was followed by a period of expanding an Inland Waterways hire fleet, in the early 1960s, and setting up one of the first cabin cruiser production flow lines, as well as a marine engineering works, in the middle 1960s.

Later experience encompassed building steel and wooden inshore fishing vessels, up to 55ft in length, yard repair work, marina management and custom boat building.

Production of competition and cruising yachts, between 22ft and 34ft, from the lamination of the GRP mouldings to the finished boat, completed a thorough technical and practical grounding in the marine trade.

Geoffrey O'Connell's highly personalised style of writing not only encompasses books on yacht building and maintenance but humour, a series of GROC's Greek island travel guides, as well as a magnum opus concerning the history of Southwick village.

By the same author:
BOAT BOOKS
The Boat Building Book
The Boat Owners Maintenance Book

LOCAL HISTORY
Secretive Southwick - Domesday to D-Day
Southwick - the D-Day Village that went to War

GUIDE BOOKS
GROC'S Candid Guides to:
Corfu & The Ionian Islands
Crete
Rhodes & The Dodecanese Islands
The Cyclades Islands
Samos & The NE Aegean Islands
The Greek Mainland Islands (Argo-Saronic & Sporades)
Athens & Travelling the Greek Islands
GROC's Companion Guide to the Greek Islands

HUMOUR
Divorce Without Remorse

**About
The Collaborator**

Paul Sumpner, aged 26, served a four year electronics apprenticeship with Marconi Underwater Systems Ltd. After successfully completing an HND in electronics, he joined Stowe Marine Equipment Ltd, manufacturers of boat electronic instruments, where he is now their Product Support Manager.

Photographed by Michelle Jeram

CONTENTS

ILLUSTRATIONS

INTRODUCTION

The purpose, in fact the corner-stone, of this book is to expose the 'Black Magic' that cloaks the subject of the repair and maintenance of marine electrics - the Achilles heel of most boat owners.

A step-by-step approach to the subject has been adopted, in order to facilitate a reader's 'tip-toe' through the mystique of 12 and 24 volt power. Certainly, once the contents of The Marine Electrics Book have been absorbed, most owners will not only be able to save money on expert's charges, but, perhaps, most importantly, will be able to rest assured that most, if not all problems can be solved.

Prior to signing off, I must express sincere thanks to my friend and collaborator in this venture - Paul Sumpner. He has 'partnered' me to the point of co-authorship, and was mainly responsible for the initial draft notes, from which the final manuscript has been crafted. Without Paul I would have been far less assured as to the veracity of the information herein. If that was not enough, he, and his wife Kay, also assisted in the task of tirelessly proof-reading.

Geoffrey O'Connell
April 1991

CHAPTER ONE

TOOLS OF THE TRADE
& PRACTICAL SKILLS

This chapter deals with the practical aspects of marine electrics, vis-a-vis the necessary tools, as well as the skills and techniques required to use them. Arguably, it is axiomatic that the more tools an owner has, the more likely he (or she) will be able to install, supplement and repair any system or installation. However, even the most comprehensive of tool kits will be found wanting, from time to time, and certainly cannot guarantee proficiency or knowledge. Without doubt, space and practicality will force a compromise between owning too many or having too few 'thingumabobs'.

The following represents the optimum tool kit to enable an owner to tackle most electrical jobs and repairs. For those who find this too extensive (and expensive), the items asterisked might well be considered essential.

An 'ideal' Tool Kit

* Electrical meter
* Wire cutters
* Wire strippers
* Stanley knife
* 2mm flat blade screwdriver
* 4mm flat blade screwdriver
  6mm flat blade screwdriver
* Small Philips screwdriver
* Medium Philips screwdriver

Large Philips screwdriver
Snipe nosed pliers
Small adjustable spanner
Universal pliers
* Set of miscellaneous crimps
* Crimp tool (for fastening, or 'crimping' on electrical connectors)
* Supply of spare fuses
Piece of fine wet & dry sandpaper
Bag of miscellaneous cable ties
12V soldering iron (25 watts minimum)
Reel of multi-core solder
Hand or cordless drill
Tape measure
Silicone grease or Vaseline
* Can of water repellant cum rust penetrator spray (such as WD40)
Reel of 1.5mm^2 electrical wire (14/0.30mm, with an amperage of 12.75)
Tube of silicone rubber
2 strips of terminal/chocolate block.

Basic Equipment 'User Friendly' Skills

With the exception of the electrical meter, which is detailed in Chapter 4, the listed items are fairly commonplace. Thus, it has been assumed that their particular application will be understood by readers, even if the correct techniques in using them, may not be known. If this is the case, the following hints should 'reveal' all to the unsure novice, and can be skipped by the skilled hand!

Preparation of Cable Ends

The covering of multiple cored cables (inside which are contained a number of separately insulated wires) must first be cut back before the wires can be used (*See* Illustration 1).

Illustration One   Preparation of Cable Ends

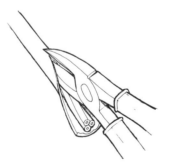 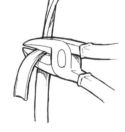

Fig 1A   Split the outer sheath as far back as required, using a pair of wire cutters,

Fig 1B   ...then bend back the outer sheath and cut off the excess.

NOTE: Care should be taken not to accidentally cut, nick or damage the insulation of the individual wires (or one's fingers!), whilst cutting the sheath.

Use a pair of (wire) strippers to remove the insulation from the individual wires. Experienced electricians carry out this task using cutters, but it is all too easy to damage, or cut off one or more of a wire's strands. Two popular types of wire strippers are sketched in Illustration 2.

Illustration Two   Wire Strippers

Fig 2A

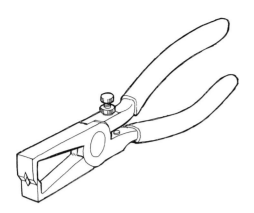

A traditional pair of wire strippers. In the jaws are two sharp 'V' notches that can cut through rubber or PVC type insulation. Turning the adjusting screw sets the minimum distance of the jaw's aperture, thus allowing the insulation to be removed, without damaging the strands of wire.
To use them:
1. Turn the adjustment screw so that the jaws, when fully closed, cut the insulation, but not the wire. Tighten the lock-nut.
2. Place the wire in the jaws and squeeze the handles.
3. Rotate the tool through ½ turn, to completely cut the insulation.
4. Firmly pull the tool back, thus stripping off the covering and exposing the strands, being careful not to twist or bend the tool out of line with them, so as not to cut through the strands.

Fig 2B

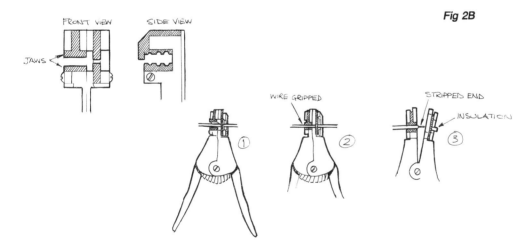

A more modern, expensive alternative to the wire stripper sketched in Fig A, but easier to use. Simply place the wire in the correct jaws and squeeze the handles. The type illustrated has a series of very sharp edged circular holes that only cut through the insulation.

Fig 2C

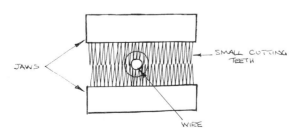

Other strippers have an array of small, sharp teeth sprung in such a way that the teeth in contact cut into the insulation, but not the strands.

The 'circular hole stripper' (Illustration 2, Fig B) usually produces a cleaner cut in the insulation but requires the user to select the right sized hole, for the size of wire, and then locate the wire in the relevant opening. The 'sprung teeth' tool (Illustration 2, Fig C) strips any size of wire, as the tines shape themselves around the contour of the cable. The amount of spring pressure is usually adjustable to suit the size and type of wire. Once a wire has been stripped, the strands should be twisted tightly together, using fingers or, snipe nosed/universal pliers (Ilustration 3). If for no other reason, this makes the strands more manageable, especially when they are to be inserted through or into a small hole.

Illustration Three   Twisting Wire Strands Together

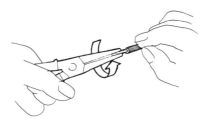

Connecting to a Threaded Terminal

Although not now commonly deployed, it is sometimes necessary to connect a wire to a threaded terminal (Illustration 4, Figs A & B).

Illustration Four   Connecting to a Threaded Terminal

Fig 4A

Having prepared the cable end, as previously detailed, the exposed wire is formed into a loop large enough to fit over the threaded terminal, usually with a pair of snipe or long nosed pliers. It is important that the wire is looped in a clockwise direction, thus ensuring that, when the nut is tightened down, the wire is not forced outwards by the turning movement of the nut and washer.

Fig 4B   A cleaner, generally preferred method is to fit a crimped terminal end.

Connecting to a Terminal/ 'Chocolate' Block

A popular method of connecting pairs of wires to each other, or connecting wires to an instrument, is to use terminal (or 'chocolate') blocks (Illustration 5, Fig A). (The term 'chocolate' block is derived, I imagine, from their shape resembling a bar of Galaxy!).

Illustration Five   Connecting to a Terminal 'Chocolate' Block

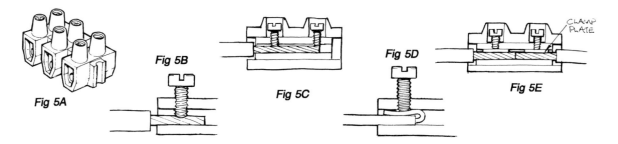

Undo the screw of the terminal block (Fig B) until there is sufficient room to insert the bared wire end into the block. The wire should be pushed in until the insulation begins to enter the block, but not so far that the screw tightens down on the insulation, rather than the bared wires, nor so far that the wires enter the 'opposing' chamber of the block (Fig C).

An alternative is to bend the stripped wire end back over the insulation and tighten down on the pair (Fig D). This removes the stress of any pull or twist from the bare wire alone.

Over-enthusiastic use of the screwdriver can result in the screw biting partly through the wire, thus a praiseworthy alternative is to use terminal blocks with a clamping plate on to which the screw tightens down (Fig E). This ensures even pressure over the wire strands and, generally, gives better results.

Probably the most popular method of joining wires together, or to electrical equipment, is with the use of crimp connections. The only other popular, 'boating' procedure is soldering. It is arguable which discipline is electrically and mechanically preferable. Soldered joints tend to be fairly brittle, especially if poorly made, and can suffer from bi-metallic corrosion in a damp environment. However, a well-executed soldered joint should last longer than crimps, the latter tending to corrode more easily.

Crimped Connections vis a vis Soldered

Without doubt crimp connections are much easier and quicker to make. The joint relies upon the wire and the crimp being clean and mechanically compressed tightly together, thus producing a good electrical connection (Illustration 6).

Crimps

Illustration Six   Crimps

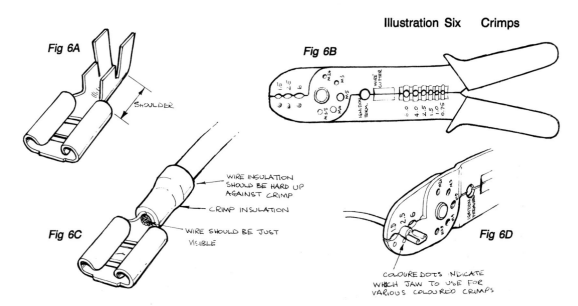

To use a crimp, strip the insulation of the wire back for the length of the insulation shoulder of the crimp (Fig A), twist the bare strands together and insert them into the crimp.

To effect the most efficient compression joint a specific tool is available (Fig B), and can be purchased complete with a set of mixed crimps, in a box. Fig C sketches the 'proper' implement.

Crimps commonly come in three different sizes to suit different gauges of wire and their insulation is colour coded:

Crimp Colour	Wire Size (AWG)
Red	22 to 18
Blue	16 to 14
Yellow	12 to 10

To ensure the best possible connection, always use the smallest crimp that will fit on to the particular wire. Place the wire into the correct jaw position, for the crimp size, and squeeze the handles together until the jaws touch (Fig D). If an unsatisfactory, loose joint occurs, then the crimp should be cut off, and a new one used to remake the connection.

Soldering

Soldering is one of the most skilled of all the practical boat electrics techniques and it is easier to perform the task badly, than well (it would be, wouldn't it?). In fact, probably more problems are caused through faulty soldering than any other connection methods.

The process is one of joining two metal objects together. It relies upon a chemical reaction between the solder (which is an alloy of tin and lead) and the surfaces of the two metal objects to be united. To enable the reaction to take place, heat must be applied (approximately 220°C), causing the solder to melt, at which stage the reaction between the solder and the surfaces of the metal objects takes place. To 'jolly' along the 'affair', a substance known as flux is employed. The Flux:-

(a) Speeds up the heat transfer.

(b) Prevents oxidation of the solder or metals.

(c) Helps to clean the surface of the metals, by removing grease and tarnish.

Nowadays the solder usually used for electrical and electronic work has the flux incorporated in a cored form (Illustration 7).

Illustration Seven   Cored Solder

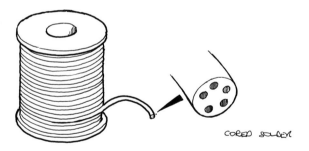

CORED SOLDER

However, it is still possible to purchase solder and flux separately, which is desirable for larger solder joints. The flux paste can be painted on to the metals to be joined and the solder dipped into the flux, before making the soldered joint. Solder should have 60% tin to 40% lead content and the flux should be active and non-corrosive.

To provide the necessary heat, in the right area, to achieve a 'good', soldered joint, has resulted in the development of the soldering iron (Illustration 8, Fig A). This is basically an electric heating element, with a handle. When electricity is applied, the element gets hot and heats the 'bit'. The latter is the part of the soldering iron placed in contact with the metal objects to be soldered and is usually made from copper - a good conductor of heat. Some copper bits are iron plated and these tend to last longer than unplated bits, which often become pitted (Illustration 8, Fig B). When this occurs they should be 'dressed' (Illustration 8, Fig C).

Illustration Eight   A Soldering Iron

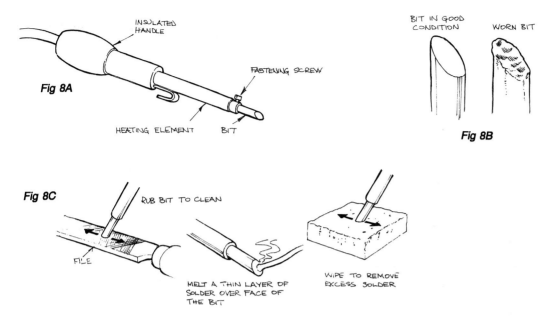

INSULATED HANDLE

FASTENING SCREW

Fig 8A

HEATING ELEMENT   BIT

BIT IN GOOD CONDITION   WORN BIT

Fig 8B

Fig 8C

RUB BIT TO CLEAN

FILE

MELT A THIN LAYER OF SOLDER OVER FACE OF THE BIT

WIPE TO REMOVE EXCESS SOLDER

Turn off the soldering iron and allow it to cool down; remove the bit and place in a vice; file the face until it is smooth and flat; replace the bit in the soldering iron, and turn the power on. As soon as the bit is hot enough, 're-tin' the end and then wipe off the excess solder.

Soldering 'Secrets'

Tinning

Nearly all solder joints consist of connecting a wire to 'something'. One of the secrets, or tricks of the trade, is to 'tin' the two items that are to be soldered together. To 'tin' a wire, first strip the insulation, then twist the exposed strands through 360°, in order to keep them together. Place the soldering iron bit against the bare strands and feed solder on to the face of the bit. Once the solder starts to flow, move the iron and the solder up the wire until the insulation is reached. Remove the iron and solder, allowing the wire to cool down (Illustration 9). 'Tinning' of other metal objects is done in a similar manner, ensuring that a layer of solder flows across the proposed point of contact with the wire.

Illustration Nine   'Tinning'

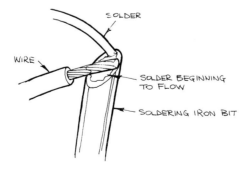

SOLDER

WIRE

SOLDER BEGINNING TO FLOW

SOLDERING IRON BIT

Mechanical Joints

The plan of action above makes it easier to carry through the second 'secret' in achieving an excellent soldered connection ...that is, making a satisfactory mechanical joint, prior to soldering. The type depends upon the items to be soldered together. Illustration 10 sketches four different mechanical joints, for four different situations.

Illustration Ten   Mechanical Joints For Soldering

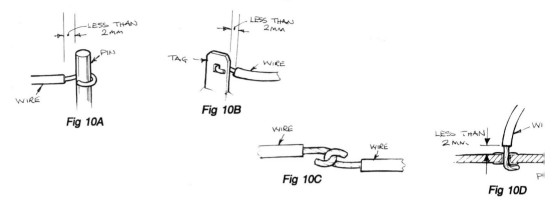

The method deployed in Fig A is used when connecting a wire to a round pin or terminal post. Once the wire has been tinned, form a small loop (using snipe or long nose pliers) and place it over the pin. Squeeze the loop of wire, with the pliers, so that it grips the pin tightly enough, that the wire can be released without falling off the pin.

The method Illustrated in Fig B is used to connect a wire to a tag or lug. Once the wire has been tinned, insert it into the slot of the tag, bend it back on itself, using pliers, and then squeeze and compress the wire up against the tag. Once again, if carried out correctly, the wire, when released, should not fall off of the tag.

The method depicted in Fig C is used to connect two pieces of wire together. After the wires have been tinned, form them into small hooks, loop and then squash them together, with pliers, so that they do not separate when released.

The method sketched in Fig D is used to connect a wire to an electronic printed circuit board (PCB). After tinning the wire, insert it into the relevant hole in the PCB and then bend over the piece that pokes through the other side of the board, so that the wire does not easily drop out of the hole, when let go.

After an acceptable mechanical joint is achieved, it is a lot easier to 'conjure up' a good soldered joint. But, to further the chances, first clean the soldering iron bit on a damp sponge, or cloth (to remove any old solder residue), then place the bit against the two pieces of metal to be soldered. It is important to try and heat both, equally, to approximately the temperature of the iron, prior to introducing the solder, thus ensuring a good joint.

Once ready, the solder should first be touched against the iron and then, as soon as it starts to flow, moved to the opposite side of the connection, in order to ensure there is an even amount of solder, all around the joint (Illustration 11).

Illustration Eleven   Soldering

It is important to remove the solder a fraction of a second earlier than the iron is removed, otherwise a 'solder spike' may form. Bad joints can also be caused by too hot, or too cool a soldering iron.

Pointers to a good job include a shiny appearance, that the solder has run round the contours of the joint evenly, and the absence of 'solder spikes'. Alternatively a poor job usually has a dull, speckled appearance and may well be a round blob, only making contact on part of the joint (Illustration 12).

Illustration Twelve Good & Bad Soldering

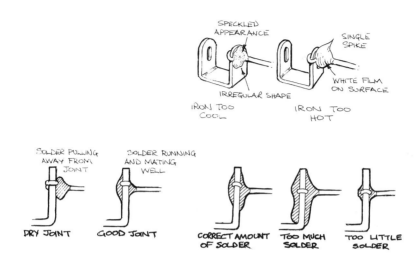

A bad joint may be caused by a number of factors, but common causes are: dirty/tarnished metals being joined; too much heat; too little heat; movement of the joint during cooling; and not enough application of flux.

A major soldering problem is that God simply did not give man (or woman) enough hands. With the solder in one 'paw', and the iron in the other, it is difficult to hold the wire steady, which is why a satisfactory, mechanical joint is so useful. A last tip is to 'have handy' a small, portable vice with which to support the wire, or the item being soldered.

CHAPTER TWO

ELECTRICAL THEORY

I hope readers are not tempted to skip this chapter, as herein is the font of all electrical wisdom. Furthermore, it will probably be necessary to return to the 'knowledge' herein, on more than a few occasions.

Little or no electrics know-how may be possessed at the outset, nor, for that matter, any idea of nuclear physics, or Einstein's Theory of Relativity. But... you may surprise yourself and master the contents, when all will be revealed - and that's from one dumbo to another!

Those in the know often maintain that Ohms Law is the lynch pin, the fundamental bedrock of electrics, but it is arguable that the 'golden rivet', the nugget, is the Power formula. This advises that Power (watts) = Voltage (V) x Current (amps, or A). *See* Page 19, and do not forget to always refer back to this premise.

From the mists of time and those long forgotten chemistry and physics lessons, will be remembered the Atom. Perhaps more relevant are the half-recollected newspaper articles about splitting the wretched things. To recap, an Atom is made up of Protons, Neutrons and Electrons. Moreover, in some situations, Electrons can be made to move from Atom to Atom - referred to as Current flow. Where Electrons are on the move, some Atoms must be losing Electrons and some gaining them, with a resultant imbalance. As nature, for all intents and purposes, attempts to maintain a balance, the extra Electrons possess a force, which strives to return them to the Atoms that have lost them. This force is named Voltage, and where a Voltage is present, Electrons (or Current) try to move.

The Power Formula

The Electron & Current Flow

Atoms

Voltage

Voltage, Current & Resistance

Atoms with extra Electrons are said to be positive (+ve), Atoms that have lost Electrons are said to be negative (-ve), and Electrons (or Current) attempt to move (or flow) from positive to negative (and this is the easy bit!).

For Current to move there must be a Voltage (similar to water pressure causing water to circulate). The amount of Current that flows depends on:-

(a) The size of the Voltage - the larger the Voltage the more Current that can circulate.

(b) The type of material through which a Current must flow. Some materials, such as gold, copper, carbon and silicon, allow Current to move through very easily, and are called Conductors. Other materials, including plastics, rubber and wood, permit Current to move only with difficulty, and are called Insulators.

Conductors

Insulators

Resistance

The measure of a material's ability to tolerate Current flow is expressed in terms of its Resistance. The larger the Resistance, the harder it is for Current to flow. If the Current cannot flow, then electric circuits will not work.

Volts, Amps & Resistance

Voltage is measured in Volts (V), Current is measured in Amperes (A), (where 1 Ampere is equivalent to approximately six million, million, million Electrons flowing through a substance every second), and Resistance is measured in ohms.

Circuits

A Circuit is a collection of wires and components connected together (Illustration 13).

Illustration Thirteen   A Simple Electrical Circuit

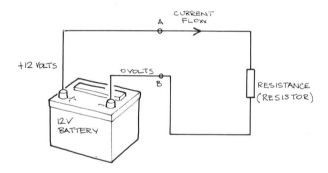

To point A is applied a voltage of 12 volts, whilst point B has zero volts, thus making point A more positive than point B. As a voltage difference exists between the two points, a current will flow from positive (+ve) to negative (-ve).

In Illustration 13 the current is shown flowing through a resistance, which could be any electrical component, such as a light, bilge pump or a radio. Even electrical wires impede the flow of a current and so possess a (slight) resistance. Despite this, for the moment, for the ease of readability and fluency, the resistance of wires, connectors, fuses and switches (in the 'on' position) are assumed to be zero - or perfect conductors.

Ohm's Law

Voltage, Current and Resistance are inextricably linked, an affiliation discovered and defined by George Simon OHM (1787-1854). This relationship, referred to as Ohm's Law, states that:-

Voltage (V) = Current (A) x Resistance (ohms.).

From this equation others naturally follow including:-

Current (A) = Voltage (V) ÷ Resistance (ohms),

Resistance (ohms) = Voltage (V) ÷ Current (A).

With these to hand, and with any two of the three values known, it is possible to calculate the Current, Resistance or Voltage, in any electrical circuit, as detailed in Illustrations 14, 15 and 16.

Illustration Fourteen   Current Calculation

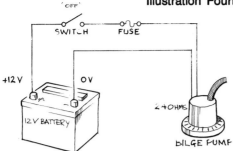

The bilge pump motor in this example, has a resistance of 24 ohms. To calculate the current flowing to the bilge pump, when the switch is closed (or switched on), and hypothesising that the switch, fuse and wiring possesses no resistance:-

The only resistance in the circuit is the 24 ohms of the bilge pump/motor. The battery is providing 12V of voltage to the circuit. With the known values of the resistance and voltage, to calculate the current, use the equation:-

Current = Voltage ÷ Resistance
Thus Current = 12V ÷ 24 ohms
Therefore Current = ½A.

Illustration Fifteen   Resistance Calculation

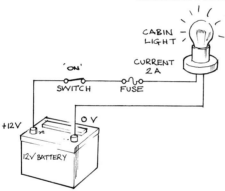

If the 12V battery is providing 2 amperes of current to light the bulb, to calculate the resistance of the cabin light, use the equation:-

Resistance = Voltage ÷ Current
Thus Resistance = 12V ÷ 2A
Therefore Resistance = 6 ohms

Illustration Sixteen   Voltage Calculation

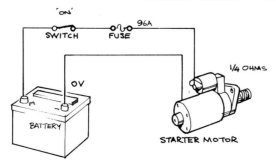

With a starter motor having a resistance of 0.25 ohms and a current flow of 96 amperes, to calculate the voltage of the battery:-

Voltage = Current x Resistance
Thus Voltage = 96A x 0.25 ohms
Therefore (Battery) Voltage = 24V

More About Circuits

Series Circuits

Basically there are two methods of connecting electrical Circuits - in Series or in Parallel. Series Circuits are where all the components are connected one after the other. In the example sketched in Illustration 17, the 12 volt battery forces current to flow through each of the bulbs in turn, causing them to light. The same amount of current flows through each bulb because all the current that leaves the +ve terminal of the battery must return to the -ve terminal. The amount of current depends on the total resistance of the three bulbs and the total voltage.

Illustration Seventeen   A Series Circuit

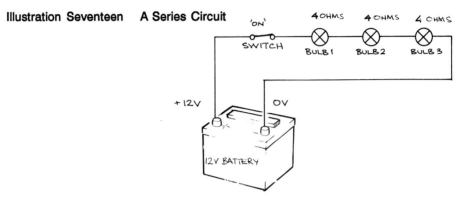

To calculate the total value of resistance in a Series Circuit add together the resistances.
   Total Resistance = The Resistance of bulb 1 + bulb 2 + bulb 3
   Thus Total Resistance = 4 ohms + 4 ohms + 4 ohms
   Therefore Total Resistance = 12 ohms

To calculate the current flowing in the Circuit, use our 'old friend', Ohms Law:-
   Current = (Battery) Voltage ÷ Total Resistance
   Thus Current = 12V ÷ 12 ohms
   Thus Current = 1A (amp)

In the example set out in Illustration 17, the current, which has been calculated to be 1 Ampere, flows through the switch into bulb 1. Here it meets a resistance that tries to stop the current from passing. In order to force the current through the resistance of bulb 1 some of the voltage is expended, or 'used up'. Thus the current, which flows into bulb 2, will not possess the full 12 volts of the battery to 'hasten it on its way', but a reduced voltage. The same will happen after the current has flown through bulb 2, but with an even more reduced voltage left to force the current through bulb 3. This effect is referred to as Voltage Drop.

Voltage Drop

Voltage Drop occurs whenever and wherever a current flows through a resistance. The amount of Voltage Drop can be calculated in the same manner as ascertaining voltage, using Ohm's Law. For example, to calculate the Voltage Drop across bulb 2, in Illustration 17, it is first necessary to know the resistance of bulb 2, as well as the current flowing through it:-
   Volt Drop for bulb 2 = Current x Resistance
   Thus Volt Drop for bulb 2 = 1A x 4 ohms
   Therefore Volt Drop for bulb 2 = 4V

In this example as bulb 1 and bulb 3 have the same value of resistance, and the same current flows through them, then the Voltage Drop across each of them must also be 4V. It is interesting to note that the Voltage Drop across each bulb, if added together, is equal to 12V (4V + 4V + 4V), establishing that, in a series circuit:-
   The sum of the Voltage Drops = The total voltage.

Because everything is connected in line, one after another, in a series circuit, if a break in the circuit occurs then the current stops flowing, and the circuit stops working. In Illustration 17, if the switch is turned off, or a bulb blows, then all the bulbs go out. A good example of this phenomena is the family Christmas tree lights. They are usually wired in series - and most of us must have spent hours trying to find the elusive loose bulb! Items wired in series include switches (connected in series with the item they are to turn on and off), and fuses (which are wired in series with the item they are to protect).

Parallel Circuits are connected together, as detailed in Illustration 18.

Parallel Circuits

Illustration Eighteen   A Parallel Circuit

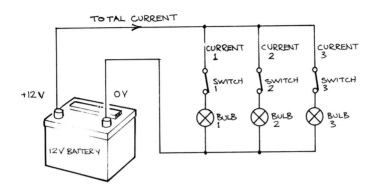

The size of each of the three currents, current 1, current 2 and current 3, depends on the resistance of the relevant bulb.

For example, if bulb 2 had a resistance of 6 ohms, then using Ohm's Law, current 2 would be:-

Current = Voltage ÷ Resistance

Therefore Current 2 = 12V ÷ 6 ohms

Thus Current 2 = 2A

This illustration details the difference between Parallel and Series Circuits, wherein each bulb, in the parallel arrangement, is directly connected to the 12V battery. This allows each bulb to receive 12 volts, rather than the 4V in the Series Circuit example (*See* Illustration 17). The current from the battery splits into three smaller currents, which, if added together, equal the total current.

The advantage of wiring any electrical item in Parallel is that each Parallel arm of the circuit is independent of the other (unlike a Series Circuit). Referring to the Illustrations 17 and 18, a bulb blowing, or a switch being turned off, in the Series Circuit turns all the bulbs off. In a Parallel Circuit any of the bulbs could blow, or be turned off, and the two remaining bulbs would continue to work.

Another example may highlight the advantage of Parallel Circuits. For instance, where installing a domestic water pump, if it was not wired in parallel with, for example, a VHF radio, but in series, then, when the VHF radio was turned on, so would be the pump! (Illustration 19).

Illustration Nineteen   Series vis-a-vis Parallel Circuit

Fig 19A   A Series Wired domestic water pump and VHF radio.

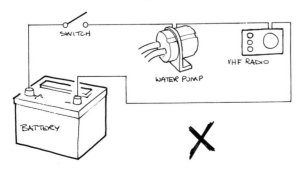

When the switch is turned on for the VHF radio - whoops, on goes the water pump!

Fig 19B   A Parallel Wired domestic water pump

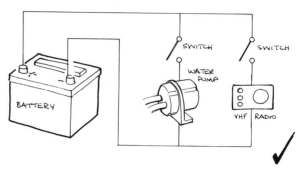

A much better idea!

This in-built advantage has resulted in wiring in Parallel being the accepted method of installing marine electrics. The fuse box is usually the point at which the current is split, and from whence it is routed to lighting circuits, instrument circuits, pumps, and so on. Each Parallel arm of the circuit should have its own fuse.

Illustration 20 highlights the sort of calculations that may have to be made in respect of fuse values and ratings. Illustration 20, Fig A, sketches the wiring circuit for a small craft's interior equipment. In this case the fuse is just one of probably eight or more, and fuses two cabin lights and a toilet light (both of which have individual switches, wired in series), as well as a radio.

Illustration Twenty   Parallel Circuit Fuse Calculations

Fig 20A

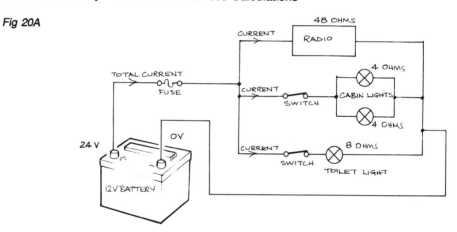

To determine the size of fuse to be fitted, it is necessary to calculate the total current required, when all the items are switched on.

In this example, the boat has a 24 volt battery installed. The full 24 volts will be applied to the radio, as well as both cabin and the toilet lights. Using Ohm's Law, the current flowing through each item is:-

    (a) Current (radio) = Voltage ÷ Resistance
        Therefore Current (radio) = 24V ÷ 48 ohms
        Thus Current (radio) = ½A

    (b) Current (toilet light) = 24V ÷ 8 ohms
        Current (toilet light) = 3A

    (c) Current (cabin light) = 24V ÷ 4 ohms
        Current (cabin light) = 6A

Both cabin lights are wired in parallel and having the same resistance, they must each draw 6 amps of current.

With Parallel Circuits the total current is the sum of all the individual currents, which equals:-

Current for radio	.50A
Current for toilet light	3.00A
Current for one cabin light	6.00A
Current for other cabin light	6.00A
Therefore the Total current =	15.50A

Allowing a safety factor, and using the empirical rule for fuse ratings, vis-a-vis the current rating, in which the fuse rating should be some one and a half times the size of the current rating, in this case a 25A fuse would be ideal.

Always fit a fuse of a greater rating than the theoretical value of the maximum current, thus incorporating some leeway. This not only allows for slight variations in the power consumption of supposedly identical replacement items, but also for any changes in the resistance of fittings as they become older, which often occurs. As a guideline the total current in normal use should be about two-thirds of the fuse's value. Conversely the fuse rating should be some one and a half times the actual current loading.

The circuit sketched in Illustration 20, Fig B, outlines the wiring of some navigation instruments, on a small power boat. It is intended to add a satellite navigation (Sat-Nav) unit by wiring it in parallel with the existing depth sounder and log. To establish if the existing fuse is large enough, to supply the extra current required, refer to the illustration's annotation.

Fuse Ratings

Fig 20B

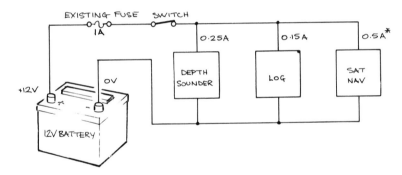

Usually instrument instruction manuals quote the maximum current for their equipment, which in this example is 0.5 amps. Knowing the current required by each instrument, the total current can be calculated as follows:-

Depth sounder current	0.25A
Log current	0.15A
Sat-Nav current	0.50A
Therefore the Total current =	0.9A

Using the empirical rule for fuse ratings, the fuse would have to be:-
0.9A x 1.5 = 1.35A, or say 1.5A.

Incidentally, if the 1A fuse was left in place, after the addition of the Sat-Nav, it would probably work, but the fuse might well be stressed and its life-span impaired. In considering fuse ratings it must be borne in mind much electrical equipment (including motors, pumps and navigation instruments) initially draws a higher than normal current, when first switched on. This is called 'Surge' or 'Turn on' Current, and can be considerably in excess of the normally required current. As the name implies, it only lasts for a short period of time, but may cause under-rated fuses to blow. In this particular example the fuse should be upgraded to at least 1.5A.

'Surge' or 'Turn on Current'

To make a piece of electrical equipment work it must be provided with power, that is there must be voltage across it and a current flowing through it. Electrical Power is measured in Watts, and can be calculated as follows:-
Power(watts) = Voltage (V) x Current (A).

Electrical Power Watts

Nearly all marine electrical equipment is 'labelled' with its particular power consumption. If not, the figure will almost certainly be detailed in the instruction/fitting manual.

In the examples to date, the resistance of bulbs, pumps and motors has been given, in order to allow the various currents and voltages to be calculated, using Ohms Law. However, in 'real life', the resistance of a bulb or a pump rarely needs to be known.

For instance, a bulb is unlikely to have the resistance indicated, but usually has the voltage and wattage information detailed. This could be 12V and 24W. The 12V indicates that it is designed to work from a 12V supply, and the 24W denotes that the bulb has 24 watts power consumption.

To calculate the current flowing through the bulb, use the formula for power, where:-

Power = Voltage x Current
Or: Current = Power ÷ Voltage
Thus Current = 24W ÷ 12V
Therefore Current = 2A

If the Resistance of the bulb is then required, it can be calculated, using Ohm's Law:-

Resistance = Volts ÷ Current
Thus Resistance = 12V ÷ by 2A
Therefore Resistance = 6 ohms

Power
Consumption

Power Consumption is a very important consideration, where boats are concerned, as there is only so much power available. Unlike (most) houses, where the amount of electrical power available is, to all intents and purposes, limitless, on a boat power is limited to the capacity of the batteries.

Battery Power Required

The 'fluence', or Power of a Battery is measured in ampere-hours (Ah). This loosely means that a battery rated at, say, 100 Ah could give 100 A of current for 1 hour, alternatively 1A for 100 hours, or 4A for 25 hours, or any multiple combination of amps and hours. When considering the size of battery/batteries to purchase, it is very important to calculate the overall electrical power requirement of the particular craft.

The following details the computations required:-
(a) First list the electrical items in normal use, and how long they are 'live' during an average 24 hour period.

Battery
Efficiency
Factor

(b) Using the graph sketched in Illustration 21, calculate the Efficiency Factor for each item. This is necessary because the quicker a battery is discharged, the less efficient it becomes. Most batteries' capacity rating is based on the battery being discharged over a 20 hour period. If the battery is discharged in less than 20 hours, then it will be less efficient, and will not provide the total power.

Illustration Twenty One   Efficiency Factor Graph

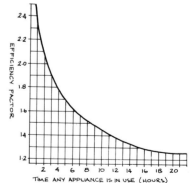

(c) Multiply the current of any individual electrical item (found by dividing its Power Consumption by the battery voltage) by the 'guesstimated' number of hours it will be 'live', and by the Efficiency Factor.
(d) Total the Ampere-hours for all items.
(e) Where only a single battery is fitted, rather than two batteries - one for starting and one for general use - then add in the starter motor's Ampere-hour requirement (as averaged in Illustration 22) to the total, as calculated in (d).

(f) Where two batteries are fitted, the starter battery should have a capacity equal to or greater than the starter motor's requirements, as indicated in Illustration 22. The other, 'domestic' battery must have a capacity equal to or greater than the total calculated in (d).

Illustration Twenty Two   Starter Motor Amp/Hour Requirements

Engine capacity	Inboard petrol engines	Inboard diesel engines
1299 cc & under	Average: 45 Amp-hours (Ah)	65 Ah
1999 cc & under	65 Amp-hours (Ah)	94 Ah
2500 cc & under		108 Ah
3999 cc & under		119 Ah

These figures tend towards the 'Doomsday', as there is no allowance for the engine's(s') 'charging ability', the alternator, running during this period, and topping up the battery's available power.

But back to the calculation, as an example, a small boat has the following electrical fitments and usage:-
(1) 4 x 12 watt fluorescent lights, for 3 hours
(2) 3 x 25 watt navigation lights, for 4 hours
(3) Set of navigation instruments totalling 6 watts, for 10 hours
(4) Bilge pump & water pump totalling 24 watts, for 4 hours
(5) B/W Television 30 watts, for 2 hours
(6) Vent/extractor fans totalling 60 watts, for 1½ hours.

The craft can only accommodate a single 12V battery, which will also have to start a 2 litre inboard diesel engine.

Domestic Items	Current*		Time		Efficiency† Factor		Ampere-hours
Fluorescent lights	4.00A	x	3hrs	x	1.90	=	22.80
Navigation lights	6.25A	x	4hrs	x	1.80	=	45.00
Navigation instruments	0.50A	x	10hrs	x	1.45	=	7.25
Pumps	2.00A	x	4hrs	x	1.80	=	14.40
Television	2.50A	x	2hrs	x	2.10	=	10.50
Fans	5.00A	x	1.5hrs	x	2.20	=	16.50

Thus the minimum domestic battery capacity for the above must be:-   116.45 Ah

* Using the formula: Current = Power (watts) ÷ Voltage (volts).   † Using Illustration 21

For starting the 2 litre inboard diesel of this example, a minimum battery capacity of 95 Ampere-hours is recommended, by the engine manufacturers (See Illustration 22). Adding this requirement to the domestic total, gives a minimum battery capacity of:-
     116.45 + 95 = 211.45 Ah

As batteries are not manufactured in 'any old' Ampere-hour sizes, other than fairly large steps, it is probable that a unit of 220 Ah or 250 Ah capacity will have to be fitted.

In previously described series circuits it was apparent that any resistance, however small, would always 'use up' or drop a voltage, when a current flows. Furthermore, the voltage magnified as the current flowing increased. This effect was described as Voltage Drop.

More about Voltage Drops

For convenience's sake, up until now, it has been assumed, in the narrative, that any wiring or connections in the circuit have had no resistance - which is not true! All wires have some resistance, normally indicated as ohms per metre, and connections invariably are never perfect conductors. Thus, any wiring 'drains away' a small amount of the batteries' total output voltage, resulting in less voltage being available to the equipment, and thus less power - as Power = Voltage x Current. Unless due allowance is made for this factor, calculations will go awry.

This loss of power is unimportant if the equipment is simply a few light bulbs, but can cause problems if the item is, say, a winch motor at the far end of a long run of heavy-duty cable.

As a rule of thumb, it is generally desirable to ensure that Voltage Drop does not exceed 0.5V in a 12V system, or 1.0V in a 24V system. Assuming the battery is in good condition, this caveat determines that the voltage across a piece of equipment should never be less than 11.5V (or 23V in a 24V installation). That's all very well (I can hear a reader expostulate) but how is it possible to avoid excessive Volt Drop? Well, as Volt Drops are caused by current flowing through unwanted resistances, it is simply a case of ensuring that these are as small as practical. To achieve this, it is necessary to make certain that all:-

(a) Connections are correctly made and that mating surfaces are clean, dry and protected, after connection, by a liberal application of silicone grease or *Vaseline*.
(b) Switches, fuse holders and connectors are good quality, marine approved items.
(c) Cabling is kept as short as possible - the longer a piece of wire, the more resistance it possesses.
(d) Cabling is of a large enough to cope with the current flowing through it. The larger the diameter of a piece of wire, the less resistance it possesses (*See* Wiring Ratings, Illustration 89, Fig A, Chapter 7).

Illustration Twenty Three   Cable Resistance Calculations

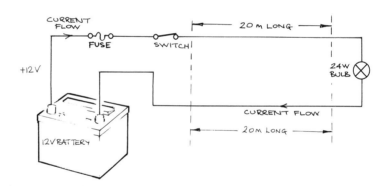

It *is necessary to fit a 24 watt tricolour navigation light at the top of a mast, requiring a 20 metre run of cable, and a two core cable is in-situ. Each core of this existing wiring has a resistance of 12.57 ohms per 1000 metres.*

To calculate the Volt Drop, and ensure the cable is adequate, it is necessary to ascertain the current flowing and the resistance of the cable. In this example, the current flows from the battery, through the fuse and switch, via the first core of the 20 metre, cable to the bulb. The current then returns to the battery through the second cable core. As a result, the current has to flow along 40 metres of cable - 20 metres there and 20 metres back.

To calculate the resistance of 40 metres of cable the required formula is:-
Calculated Resistance = Stated cable resistance x The actual cable length ÷ The cable length to which the stated resistance is related.
Therefore the Calculated Resistance = 12.57 ohms x 40m ÷ 1000m.
Thus the Calculated Resistance = 0.5 ohms

The current that flows can be calculated using the formula for power where:-
Power = Voltage x Current,
or Current = Power ÷ Voltage.

It is known that the bulb consumes 24 watts of power and the battery provides 12V of voltage, so:-
Current = Power ÷ Voltage
Therefore Current = 24W ÷ 12V
Thus Current = 2A

Knowing the total resistance of the two cores of the cable and the current that flows through them enables the voltage to be calculated, using Ohms Law, where:-
Voltage = Current x Resistance
Therefore Voltage = 2A x 0.5 ohms
Thus Voltage = 1V

As previously stated the maximum, desirable Volt Drop in a 12V system is 0.5V. The Volt Drop in this proposed circuit is 1V, therefore a thicker size of wire must be used (See Wiring Ratings, Chapter 7 for the ideal cable rating).

CHAPTER THREE

12V & 24V SYSTEMS AND 240V AC SHORE SUPPLIES

Within this book the examples of typical circuits are detailed with batteries of 12V or 24V (volt) capacity - the most common marine installations. It is interesting to note that, in the early years of automotive, and thus marine, electrics, the original voltage selected was 6V, with 12V introduced at the luxury end of the market. Over the decades the 12V systems overtook and finally supplanted the 6V 'driven' installations. Similarly, paralleling automotive design, from which many of the smaller marine engines are adapted, 12V systems are commonplace, with 24V installations used on the larger horsepower units. Year in, year out 24V systems are becoming increasingly common, and spreading down the horsepower range.

Twelve volt battery systems are smaller, lighter and cheaper than the 24V alternative. Additionally, they are generally standard equipment on the basic power units from which most marine engines are derived, thus they are the most popular, being found almost exclusively on privately owned pleasure craft.

12 Volts

On the other hand, the superior electrical qualities of 24V systems is resulting in their increasing use on larger power units, and thus the bigger boats. The pre-eminence of 24V systems is to be found 'lurking' in the formula for electrical power where:-

24 Volts
The Reason for 24 Volt Pre-eminence

Power (watts) = Voltage (V) x Current (amps).

As an example, where a 24W bulb is connected to a 12V battery, the current consumed by the bulb is 2A (using the formula in which Current (in Amps) = Power (in Watts) ÷ the Voltage:

or Current = 24 ÷ 12 = 2A.

On the other hand, a 24V battery would only have to supply 1A (Current = 24 ÷ 24 = 1A). In fact, by selecting a 24V battery, in preference to a 12V one, the amount of current flowing in any circuit can be halved. This results in thinner cables, as well as smaller switches and fuses, and voltage drop is a 'halved problem'. For instance, if a voltage drop of 1V exists in a 12V circuit, giving an 8% loss of power, in a 24V circuit it would only result in a 4% loss of power.

Extra demands on the power supply, due to boat owners wishing to enjoy ever more home comforts, as well as the benefits of the latest electronic navigation aids, is resulting in an ever-increasing number of 24V systems being installed.

AC Shore Supplies

Before elaborating in respect of the subject of Alternating Current (AC) Shore Supplies, it must remembered that 240V AC mains voltage can kill. This 'small matter' is occasionally overlooked, especially by those who might have received an electric shock from a domestic mains supply, and lived to tell the tale. But it must be borne in mind that any apparent immunity from 'shuffling off the mortal coil' was probably due to a dry, rubber-backed carpet, rubber-soled shoes and or dry hands - circumstances which increase resistance to the electricity in its attempt to 'earth out'. Conversely, on or around a boat, in a marine environment, the surroundings are much more conducive to aiding electricity on its way through the human frame, to a watery earth. After which there usually isn't much more messing about in boats!

If a boat has a 240V mains supply wired in, always disconnect it from the shore supply, prior to working on any electrics. This advice includes circumstances where it is 99.9% certain that only the 12V Direct Current (DC) circuit is involved. One other word of warning is to those considering fitting 240V sockets and a ship-to-shore cable extension - have it installed by a professional electrician, preferably with marine experience.

Certainly an AC Shore Supply is a very useful facility to have, and even though most are metered, it still works out cheaper than running up the engine. Possessing the facility to plug into a mains supply, when moored, allows an owner to 'enjoy' all the creature comforts of home! Oh, goody, goody! These might include the attributes of television, video, hi-fi, a micro-wave oven, and even a washing machine, without having to purchase expensive 12V DC versions, and the ever-present possibility of running the craft's batteries flat.

AC Installation Hints

To those aspirants determined to do-it-themselves (and there will always be someone, whatever they are advised), the following suggestions should be followed:-

(a) Keep the system simple and install the minimum number of sockets and wiring.

(b) Fit a Residual Current Device (RCD) or earth leakage detector. These basically monitor the amount of current flowing from the device down the live wire, comparing it to the current returning to the device along the neutral wire (Illustration 24). RCD's are commonly available and it cannot be too strongly emphasised that anyone having or intending to install an AC Shore Supply to a craft should have one fitted.

Illustration Twenty Four   A 240 Volt Earth Leaking Detector (or RCD)

If there is less current returning, than arrived, the RCD assumes that the lost current is electrocuting someone! To save on this 'unnecessary, energy-wasting interruption', the device breaks the live and neutral connection, thus stopping any further current flowing.

(c) Fit 15A, 3 core, rubber covered mains cable as rubber insulation tends to be more robust than PVC, being more resistant to both physical and heat abuse. Reinforcement of this suggestion is contained in an addendum to the new, British Waterways Board's 'Standards For Equipment of Boats. Herein, it is stated that where PVC covered cable comes into contact with polystyrene insulation material (widely used in Narrow Boats), the PVC becomes brittle and falls off the cable, with the resultant chance of short-circuits and fire. Additionally, it does not avoid the problem by encasing the cable in PVC trunking or conduit, for the same reactive reasons.

(d) Do not route a mains cable adjacent to 12V DC wiring, but keep all runs at least 50mm away from any other cabling. This is to minimise the risk of a mains voltage shorting across to the 12V system, as well as to stop unwanted electrical mains noise being radiated in the 12V wiring.

(e) Never use terminal blocks, or other uncovered connectors, to connect or terminate mains cables. On the contrary, always fit enclosed mains sockets or, small ABS type plastic boxes. And identify all mains cabling with warning signs.

(f) If there is any chance at all of a mains cable suffering external impact, then that cable run must be enclosed in impact-proof, plastic conduit. Incidentally, this is good practice for all cabling, but especially mains supplies, as long as the caveats indicated in item (c) are borne in mind. (*See* Illustration 100, Chapter 7).

(g) As for any cable runs (but even more so), where mains wiring passes through cut-outs and or bulkhead holes ensure, that there are no sharp edges that could cut or wear through the insulation. (*See* Illustration 100, Chapter 7).

Annual inspection/maintenance is very important once a 240V AC system is installed. The following are items to check:-

AC Inspection Tips

(a) All plugs and sockets - for burn marks or pitting, both of which are signs of arcing or overheating, caused by poor or intermittent connections.

(b) All wiring connections - to ensure that no wires have worked loose or have become weak with metal fatigue or water contamination (rust).

(c) The plug that connects to the shore supply - as this is likely to be the most 'abused' part of the system.

For those who do not wish to install a full 240V AC system, there are a number of alternatives. These include deploying:-

Alternatives to AC Shore Supplies

(1) A heavy-duty battery charger. These units can be fitted permanently in a boat, so that whenever moored at a berth, with the provision of mains supply, the charger can be plugged in and the battery charged.

The advantage of a heavy-duty battery charger, over the standard, automotive 'trickle charge' unit, is that they are powerful enough to power a limited number of other onboard electrical items. The amount of electrical equipment that can be 'driven' depends on the maximum output current that the charger can provide. Due to their size and cost, they are usually only fitted on larger boats.

Features that should be incorporated in a heavy-duty battery charger are that:-

(a) It is marinised and or possesses a British Standard Specification.

(b) It possesses the ability to power other 12V DC (or 24V) equipment, whilst charging the battery.

(c) It can monitor and indicate the battery charge state (usually by a meter or warning lights).

(d) It has short-circuit protection.

(e) It is designed for permanent connection, without overcharging the battery.

(2) An Inverter

(3) A Rotary Converter

(4) A Portable Generator.

(5) A dual voltage Alternator (12V/24V DC & 240V AC).

For more details and description in respect of Items 2, 3, 4 and 5, refer to Chapter 5.

CHAPTER FOUR

THE ELECTRICAL METER

The electrical meter is 'the' fault-finding tool for electrical circuits. Generic names for the equipment include: multi-meter, voltmeter, digital multi-meter (DMM), digital voltmeter (DVM), and AVO (amps/volts/ohms - a trade name).

Most meters allow measurements of voltage, current and resistance, and it cannot be overstressed that a meter is a necessity - if any type of fault is to be located, with the minimum amount of 'wild goose chasing'.

A rather 'doo-hickey', home-made alternative can be lashed together utilising a bulb, battery and two pieces of wire (*See* 'A simple test lamp', towards the end of this chapter).

The Analogue Meter (Illustration 25) is the oldest, simplest and cheapest type of meter. All measurements are read from the meter's scale, even if the presence of more than one scale can cause confusion. Another drawback is that these instruments are not especially robust, due to their internal moving parts.

Analogue Meters

When purchasing one, the following points should be borne in mind, namely that the unit has:-

Purchasing Points

(a) As large and clear a dial as possible
(b) 4mm test lead sockets (standard size)
(c) Minimum current ranges*

* The reason for minimum current ranges is that, in practice, current measurements are awkward to carry out and, as will become clear, are usually unnecessary.

(d) A 15V DC range for a 12V system (or a 30V DC range for a 24V system).
(e) A 250V AC range
(f) A clear and easy to follow instruction manual.
(g) The ability to be switched between ranges (as opposed to a series of sockets, in which to place the leads).
(h) An 'off' position. This puts a short across the movement, thereby damping the action and ensuring it is less vulnerable to mechanical shock.

Many auto-electricans, rather than use a multi-meter, employ a simple pair of instruments, namely an ammeter and a voltmeter.

Illustration Twenty Five   An Analogue Meter

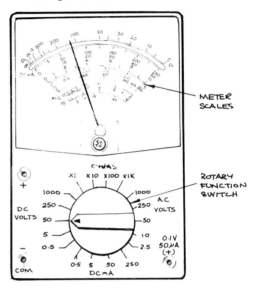

Digital Meters

Digital Meters (Illustration 26) have been available for about a decade, but only recently have the prices dropped sufficiently for them to be 'within the pocket' of most people. They are generally more rugged, reliable, accurate and easy to use than analogue meters. For a 'kick-off', a user does not have to contend with difficult-to-read scales. The values are simply read off the digital display.

Illustration Twenty Six   A Digital Meter

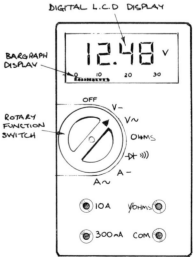

Auto-ranging

Most digital meters possess an 'Auto-ranging' facility where it is possible to measure any value from, say, a thousandth of a volt through to a thousand volts, without changing the settings. The Disadvantages of this type of meter are:-

(a) The cost - the cheapest is about twice the price of the equivalent analogue unit.

(b) They are only good at measuring constant values*. This can cause problems if, for example, a user wishes to measure the value of voltage present at a starter motor - at the very instant when the ignition key is turned.

Disadvantages

> * *The reason is due to the way they work. They 'snatch' a very quick, single measurement, which takes approximately 1/100th second. It then displays the measured value, after which there is a delay of between ½ and 1 second for the operator to read the value, after which the meter repeats the process - measure, display, wait. If the value changes during the 'wait period' it is missed.*

Thus further disadvantages are applications where a digital meter is to be used to:-

(c) Find a bad connection which is causing an indicator light to flicker, perhaps the result of moving wires.

(d) Check that the pulses from the paddle-wheel of a log transducer are reaching the display unit.

To counteract the built-in digital meter drawbacks, some recent models have a bargraph feature. This consists of a series of bars, usually situated below the digits of the display. The number of bars that turn on depends on the size of the value being measured. The meter still takes a measurement, displays and waits, but it only delays for about a tenth of a second before measuring and displaying on the bargraph again. By watching the bargraph, rather than the digits, it is possible to observe any sudden changes in the value.

When purchasing a digital meter, 'machine' plus points incorporated should include:-

Purchasing Points

(a) An 'auto-ranging' feature

(b) Compact size - some really are pocket size!

(c) Continuity bleep - when checking if a wire connects two points, the instrument will bleep if the wire is not broken. This allows an operator to concentrate visually on the job, and not the meter.

(d) Auto-power off - which saves wasted batteries if the meter is accidentally left switched on.

(e) 4mm test leads (standard size)

(f) Bargraph feature

As, boats are not the most ideal environment for electrical equipment, purchasers should not spend too much money on a meter, which may, all to easily, be accidently dropped overboard, or into the bilges.

Due to the lack of standardisation and number of different meters available, the following is only a guide, giving a general description of how to take electrical measurements. Naturally, for more specific instructions, it will be necessary to consult the manual appertaining to a particular meter.

Using a Meter

Prior to using one, always check the test probes are in good condition. If the rubber insulation is cracked, melted or damaged, purchase a new set.

It is advisable to remove personal jewellery and watches. Should a current of 100A pass through a metal object, it can cause some discomfort!

Most importantly, if a boat is connected to a 240V AC supply, and it is not the intention to measure it, then disconnect the mains, prior to carrying out any other readings.

Be the voltage AC or DC, the principle of measuring voltage is the same, namely:-

Voltage Measurement

(a) Make an educated guess at the maximum voltage to be measured. For instance, if the boat has a 12V battery, then the maximum voltage will be 12V DC*, whilst when measuring mains voltage, the maximum will be 240V AC - plus or minus 6%. Well, that is the supposed legal variation!

> * *This is an approximate figure and, as will be seen later, the voltage can be as high as 15V, or even 16V DC.*

(b) Set the meter to the next range up from the maximum voltage to be measured. For the aforementioned, this would be, respectively, 15V DC and 250V AC (Where the meter is auto-ranging, no switching is required, as it is done automatically). If unsure of the voltage to be measured, initially set the meter to the highest range and decrease, until a reading can be taken.

(c) Incidentally, to measure the voltage difference between two points of a circuit, simply place a probe at each point (Illustration 27).

Illustration Twenty Seven   Measuring Voltage Difference

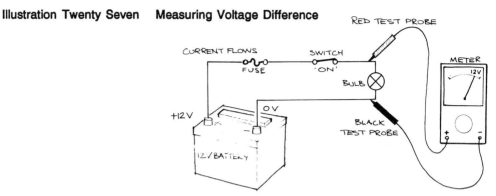

The meter should read 12V and the bulb be alight. If the probes are the wrong way round the needle will move hard up against the left-hand side of the scale. The reason is that the meter 'thinks' the voltage is negative, if a larger voltage is present, on the black test probe, than on the red. The meter's probes are only 'polarity conscious' for DC measurements and when this occurs, simply reverse the probes.

If the test probes are round the wrong way on a Digital Meter, the voltage will show as being negative, displaying a minus sign (-ve) in front of the displayed value.

Current Measurements

As with voltage, there is no difference, in principle, between AC and DC Current Measurements. Making a guess at the maximum, likely current to be measured is not as straightforward as for voltage measurements. It is recommended that the meter is set to the largest current range, and progressively decreased whilst measuring. If the worst is anticipated, then at least there will be less chance of any nasty surprises. Mind you, as most multi-meters only measure milliamps, apart from the 'full-blown' AVO type instrument, even this precaution may not save a meter.

Current Measurements monitor the current flowing through a circuit. To carry out computations it is necessary to insert the meter into the circuit, so that all the current flows through the meter (Illustration 28).

Illustration Twenty Eight   Current Measurements

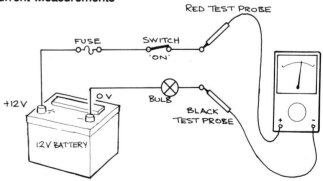

The meter displays the current flowing through the bulb, which will be lit, as the meter is part of the circuit. If the meter is removed, the bulb will extinguish (unlike the voltage example, Illustration 27, where the bulb would remain lit).

Measuring Resistance differs from evaluating voltage and current, as no power is taken from the circuit. Instead, a battery, inside the meter, causes a current to flow through the circuit to be tested. The amount of this current depends on the Resistance of the circuit.

The following procedure must be followed for Resistance Measurements:-

(a) Always ensure that the circuit being tested is switched off, as the meter's internal battery is to be used. If another voltage is present, it will result in an incorrect reading, and might 'kill' the meter.

(b) Switch the meter to Resistance and press the two test probes together. The reading should be zero ohms.

However nearly all analogue meters, and some early digital meters, require zeroing whenever carrying out Resistance Measurements, or when switching to another Resistance range. This is because the battery in the meter may be fully charged or an old unit that is nearly 'flat'. To allow for the difference in battery voltage, an ohms adjustment is usually provided that can set the meter to zero.

(c) If the meter has a zero ohms adjustment, set this so that zero is displayed when the test probes are shorted together. This adjustment is not to be confused with the mechanical zero adjustment, often to be found on analogue meters.

(d) As with current measurements, it is necessary to insert the meter into the circuit, after ensuring the battery is disconnected, placing the probes to the two points where the battery was connected (Illustration 29).

Illustration Twenty Nine   Measuring Resistance

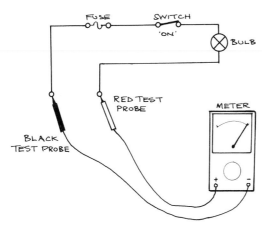

Here, the fuse, switch, bulb and all the wiring are being tested. The total resistance of each separate item within the circuit, including connections between wire and components, will be shown on the meter.

Meter users should:-

(a) Ensure that the Meter is set correctly to measure voltage, current or resistance. Measuring voltage, with the Meter set to current or resistance (or vice-versa) could damage the unit.

(b) If the Meter does not appear to be working, check that the internal battery is in good condition, then the internal fuse. The latter is often fitted to protect the instrument against large currents or voltages.

(c) Bear in mind that a large number of Meters have more than two sockets in which to plug the test probes. As well as changing the function switch to select voltage, current or resistance, it is necessary to plug the red test probe into the correct socket. If, for instance, the probe is plugged into the current socket, when measuring voltage, the Meter may be damaged.

(d) If in any doubt, double check and refer to the instrument's instructions.

(e) Proceed cautiously, ensuring that the contact points selected are clean, in order to make a good connection with the probes.

*Useful
Accessories*

(f)   If possible, place the Meter close to the contacts, so as to be able to see the reading and the placement of the probes, at the same time.

Most meters are provided with a pair of test probes (Illustration 30).

Illustration Thirty   Meter Test Probes

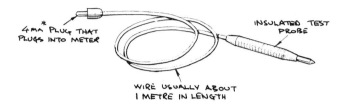

Though 4mm is the standard size for test leads, some cheaper meters are fitted with 1mm, or 2mm plugs.

For most situations these are adequate, general purpose leads. However, it is often desirable to clip one of the leads to a wire, or a connector, so that an operator only has to concentrate on holding one of the probes to the contacts. 'Crocodile clips' should be employed in these cases (Illustration 31).

Illustration Thirty One   Test Probe Crocodile Clips

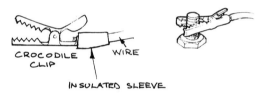

It is possible to purchase a pair of crocodile clips that can be attached to the test probes, or a set of test leads, with a 4mm plug on one end and a crocodile clip on the other.

For meters, with limited current ranges, it is possible to purchase a current 'shunt' - a very low value resistor (less than 1 ohm). When connected to a circuit, any current flowing through the shunt causes a voltage to be present across the shunt. By measuring this voltage with a meter, the current flowing in the circuit can be calculated, but ensure the chosen contacts are good, otherwise a resistance will occur.

One 'worth having' accessory is a long length of wire, with crocodile clips affixed to both ends. This can be used, to great effect, to aid testing extensive lengths of cable, such as those which 'feed' the masthead navigation lights.

**A Simple Test
Lamp**

The use of a bulb, and a couple of pieces of wire, as a means of fault-finding electrical systems, is not an earth-shatteringly new concept. This arrangement offers an inexpensive and alternative method of locating a fair number of simple defects. One outstanding advantage is that an operator can concentrate full-square on the job, the light being visible even from the corner of an eye.

The most basic Test Lamp consists of a 12V bulb (or 24V, depending on the boat's electrical system), a bulb holder, two lengths of wire (each about 1 metre long) and crocodile clips (Illustration 32).

Illustration Thirty Two   A Test Lamp

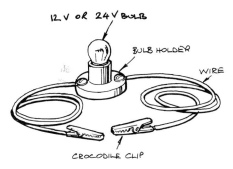

The test lamp can be used to check if a voltage is present at a piece of equipment, that appears not to work. If the lamp lights, when connected across the power connections, then it will be apparent that + 12V (or 24V) is available, and the equipment must be at fault. If, however, the test lamp does not illuminate, then further investigation will be necessary.

In conjunction with a 9V battery, a Test Lamp can be used to test the continuity of wires, or the state of fuses. This is carried out by connecting the battery, test lamp and the wire, or fuse, to be tested, in series (Illustration 33).

Illustration Thirty Three   A Continuity Test with 'The' Lamp

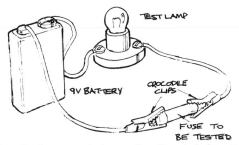

If the test lamp lights, then the fuse, or whatever other item is being tested, is working.

Test lamp exponents, prepared to expend a little more time and effort, can build a 'permanent' test lamp. An ideal set-up could be fitted in a small, black, ABS plastic box, commonly available in most electronic/electrical shops. The latter provides reasonable protection against physical damage and water ingress. The box should be big enough to house the 9V battery, and ensures the arrangement looks more professional, than a couple of lengths of wire attached to a bulb (Illustration 34).

A Professional Test Lamp

Illustration Thirty Four   A 'Professional' Test Lamp

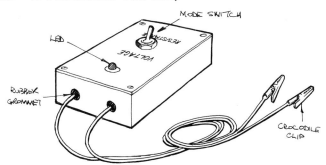

All the parts are readily available, and the whole thing, including battery, should only cost £10-£15.

A 'test lamp', fitted with a conventional bulb, will light if connected in either direction. It should be noticed that in Illustration 34 a light emitting diode (LED) is fitted, instead of a conventional bulb, but this type of light is difficult to 'see out of the corner of the eye'.

Polarity Conscious & LED's

LED's are smaller, easier to fit and are Polarity Conscious. (What!). To explain, when an electrical item is referred to as Polarity Conscious, it indicates that it will only work if the connections are made the correct way round. Typical examples of Polarity Conscious electrical items include fluorescent lights, DC motors and electronic instruments. Thus, as the LED is Polarity Conscious, it will only light if it is 'hooked-up' the right way round to a battery and can be used to check that the +12V and 0V wiring to a piece of equipment are correct.

To 'sex' or determine which are the +ve and -ve LED connections, it is only necessary to examine the plastic head of the device. It will be observed that one side is cut flat, and is not rounded, like the rest of the plastic body (Illustration 35). The leg on the flat side of the device is always the cathode, or -ve connection, and the opposite leg is the anode, or +ve connection. More often than not, one leg is shorter than the other. However, just because the cathode is the short leg on one LED, does not mean that the short leg will be the cathode on another! Moral, don't judge an LED by the length of its leg - only by the flat of its body.

Illustration Thirty Five   'Sexing' or Determining the Polarity of LED's

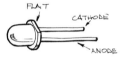

Test Lamp Circuit

The circuit diagram for an ideal test lamp box is shown in Illustration 36.

Illustration Thirty Six   Test Lamp Circuitry

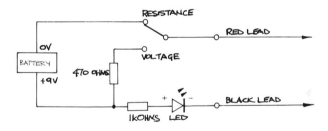

With the switch set to show voltage, the LED lights if approximately 2V, or more, is present between the two test leads. However, it will only light if the voltage on the red lead is larger, or more positive, than the voltage at the black lead. As little as 2V will only light the LED dimly, an illuminosity that increases in brightness, up to a maximum of 15V for a 12V test lamp, and 30V for a 24V test lamp.

With the test switch set to resistance, the LED lights if the resistance is less than about 10k ohms (10,000 ohms), and so may well light, even if there is a poor connection. Thus, this method is really only useful for checking fuses, or disconnected lengths of wire.

Note: For a 24V test lamp, change the 470 ohms resistor for one of 1.8k ohms (1,800 ohms).

An alternative to employing an LED is to fit a small +12V (or +24V DC) buzzer. By substituting one, for the LED, it is possible to audibly check voltage or resistance. This allows an operator to concentrate on making the connections, without constantly having to check the meter to see if the LED is lit (Illustration 37).

Illustration Thirty Seven   A Buzzer Test Lamp Circuit

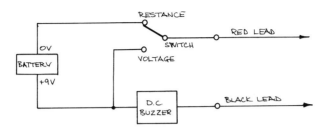

CHAPTER FIVE

GENERATING THE POWER

At the 'heart' of all marine electrical systems is the Battery. (It often seems that the most 'common' battery, fitted in a small boat, is a flat battery - but this need not be so).

The case of a Battery encloses two or more different chemicals. When combined, these cause an electrical voltage to be set up between two fixed parts, or plates, of the Battery, or cell. When electric current flows from the positive to the negative plates, a chemical reaction takes place and some of the Battery's charge is lost. (Illustration 38). The more current that flows, the larger the chemical reaction, and the more charge is lost.

Illustration Thirty Eight   The Battery Chemistry

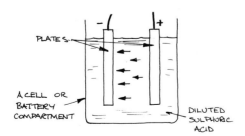

PLATES

A CELL OR
BATTERY
COMPARTMENT

DILUTED
SULPHURIC
ACID

The Chemical Reaction

When a Battery is recharged, either by a battery charger or a dynamo/alternator, the chemical reaction is reversed and power or charge is returned to the Battery. The amount of charge or power that a Battery can hold is expressed in Ampere-hours (Ah), as detailed in Chapter 2. There are a number of types of Battery available, but only two are worth considering, if on the grounds of cost alone.

Lead-Acid Batteries

The cheapest and most common type is the Lead-Acid unit (Illustration 39).

Illustration Thirty Nine   A Lead Acid Battery

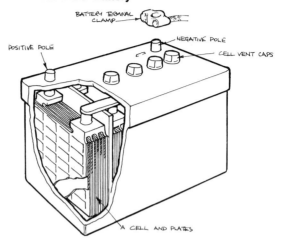

The 'Body Battery'

Nickel-Cadmium Batteries

Nickel-cadmium (Ni-cad) Batteries are more expensive than the lead-acid alternatives, and approximately twice the size. On the other hand, they more often than not have four times the life-expectancy, and can be left for long periods, such as winter lay-up, without suffering any damage due, to completely discharging.

Battery Efficiency

Both are less efficient at receiving a charge, than discharging, and, generally, should receive 1.4 times more charge than discharge. This can be achieved by increasing the charging current and or increasing the duration of charging. However, the amount of charging current can only be increased to a point, after which the battery chemicals become damaged.

Charge Rates

Generally a lead-acid battery can accept a maximum Charge Rate of approximately one tenth of its overall capacity. Thus if a battery is rated at 100 Ah, the maximum charge rate is:- 100 ÷ 10 = 10 Ah.

Nickel-cadmium batteries can, usually, be charged at higher rates - about a sixth of their capacity. A nickel-cadmium battery with a capacity of 100 Ah has a maximum charge rate of:- 100 ÷ 6 = 17 Ah.

To ensure that a battery stays well charged, it is vital to put back the energy removed. Being able to calculate the maximum Charge Rate comes in very useful, when determining the size of a particular 'charging plant'. The latter is, more often than not, an engine driven alternator, whilst in years gone by the most common unit was an engine driven dynamo. An alternator, properly matched to the battery, should be charging at

Charging Times

approximately the battery's maximum Charge Rate. With this figure to hand, it is possible to calculate how long it will be necessary to run the engine (or generator) to recharge the battery, after a day and or night's use. For example:-

A (sailing) boat, fitted with a 12V electrical system, and 100 Ah battery, sails for 8 hours. During this period the following equipment was in use:-

Item	Power Consumption (in watts)	Duration Equipment in Use
Log	0.5W	8 hrs
Echo-sounder	1.0W	8 hrs

Radio receiver	7.0W	2.00 hrs
VHF Radio	20.0W	0.50 hr
Autopilot	18.0W	3.00 hrs
Refrigerator	50.0W	3.00 hrs
Navigation lights	72.0W	1.00 hr
Cabin light	8.0W	0.75 hr
Chart light	25.0W	1.75 hrs

To work out how long the engine's alternator must be run, to replace the power taken from the battery, during this period, follow the ensuing computation.

To calculate the current provided to each piece of equipment, refer back to Chapter 2, and pluck out 'The' formula, the one that says:-
    Power (watts) = Voltage (V) x Current (A).
As the watts and the voltage are known, the current can be worked out (by taking away voltage from the right-hand side of the equation and, thus, dividing the left-hand side by the same amount). So:-
    Current (A) = Watts (W) ÷ Voltage (V).
Further, by multiplying the resultant amps by the hours of use, the Ampere-hours (Ah) of each piece of equipment can be evaluated, as follows:-

Log	=	$\frac{0.5W}{12V}$	=	0.04A	x	8.00 hrs	=	0.32 Ah
Echo sounder	=	$\frac{1.0W}{12V}$	=	0.08A	x	8.00 hrs	=	0.64 Ah
Radio receiver	=	$\frac{7.0W}{12V}$	=	0.60A	x	2.00 hrs	=	1.20 Ah
VHF Radio	=	$\frac{20.0W}{12V}$	=	1.70A	x	0.50 hrs	=	0.85 Ah
Autopilot	=	$\frac{18.0W}{12V}$	=	1.50A	x	3.00 hrs	=	4.50 Ah
Refrigerator	=	$\frac{50.0W}{12V}$	=	4.17A	x	3.00hrs	=	12.51 Ah
Navigation Lights	=	$\frac{72.0W}{12V}$	=	6.00A	x	1.00 hr	=	6.00 Ah
Cabin Light	=	$\frac{8.0W}{12V}$	=	0.67A	x	0.75 hr	=	0.50 Ah
Chart Light	=	$\frac{25.0W}{12V}$	=	2.08A	x	1.75 hrs	=	3.64 Ah

Thus, during the eight hour period the total Ah 'consumed' equals:-   30.16 Ah, or say 30.00 Ah

As lead-acid batteries are fairly inefficient, and it is not possible to extract all the energy therein, more must be generated, than is removed, in order to keep the battery fully charged. With the empirical discharge-to-charge factor of 1.4, and harking back to the lead-acid battery charge rate of a tenth - if 30 Ah has been discharged, it will be necessary to put back in:- 30 Ah x 1.4 = 42 Ah.

As the maximum charge rate of the battery is:-
    100 Ah ÷ 10 = 10A
Then the alternator will need to be run for:-
    42 Ah ÷ 10A = 4.25 hours.

Incidentally this is a considerable period of 'engine on' for a sailing boat and highlights one of the problems in keeping a battery fully charged.

Determining the State of a battery's charge can be done in a number of ways:-   *Battery State*
(a) Using a meter to measure the open circuit voltage. This is the easiest method and is

achieved by turning off the battery isolator switch, to ensure that no current is flowing from the battery, and then measuring the voltage across the battery terminals. If the voltage is between 12.5V and 12.8V, then the battery is fully charged. If, however, a voltage of between 11.5V and 11.8V is indicated, the battery is discharged, and should the voltage be less than 11V, the battery may be damaged beyond repair.

Where the reading is 11.5V, or below, peer into the filler/vent holes and ensure all the separate cells are covered by fluid. If they are not, then the readings will be low or non-existent, and those under-filled cells must be topped-up with distilled water. Do not use ordinary tap water, as the minerals naturally in solution might neutralise the battery acids. Whilst inspecting the cells, check the colour of the plates. If one or more are misty this more often than not indicates that they have collapsed and the battery is useless.

(b) Deploying an ordinary meter to measure the open circuit voltage can be misleading. Older batteries may appear to be fully charged and give a reading indicating a voltage of 12.5V to 12.8V. However, due to age, internal deterioration may have occurred, effecting the unit's ability to receive and hold a charge. A better test is to use a high rate discharge tester - basically a very low value resistor (less than 1 ohm) connected across a voltmeter. When this is placed across the battery a large current flows through the meter. If the battery is in good condition, the voltage indicated on the meter will stay at a constant value for 10 seconds, or longer. If, however, the voltage slowly decreases, during the 10 second period, then the battery is either in need of a charge, or, if after charging it still cannot maintain a constant voltage for 10 seconds, it is in need of replacement. Due to the large current that flows through the meter it is recommended this test is not carried out immediately after the battery has been charged. This is because hydrogen, and oxygen gases are released, during charging, due to the chemical reaction that takes place within the cells, and may be ignited by any sparks created when the meter is connected/disconnected. This can result in a nasty bang, in a confined space

If there is no access to a high rate discharge meter, then the same effect can be achieved by using the starter motor, as large currents are drawn during starting. Hold the starter on for approximately 10 seconds, after which, if the battery volts shows less than 9.5V, the unit is defective.

(c) Using a hydrometer - a 'clever little' device that measures the amount of acid in a battery (Illustration 40). As the battery discharges, the concentration of the acid becomes less, so measuring the acid concentration indicates the unit's condition.

Illustration Forty   The Hydrometer

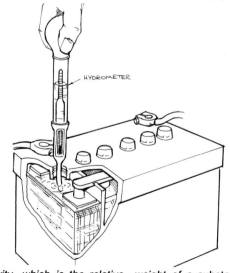

Hydrometers actually measure specific gravity, which is the relative weight of a substance, with reference to pure water. Pure water has a specific gravity of 1, while the solution (or electrolyte to give it its technical name) in a fully charged battery has a value of 1.265. As the battery discharges, so the amount of acid decreases, as does the specific gravity of the solution. A discharged battery will have a specific gravity of about 1.150.

An inexpensive hydrometer can be purchased from most car accessory shops, but be careful to purchase one designed to measure a battery's concentration, and not antifreeze, as they are calibrated differently.

Routine Maintenance of lead-acid batteries must be carried out at regular intervals. Basic requirements are to:-
(a) Check the electrolyte level, and 'top up' with distilled water, when necessary.
(b) Ensure that the battery terminals are clean and tight. A convenient method of 'doing away' with that white substance, that occurs on and around the battery poles and terminal clamps, is to wash them off with very hot water. Subsequently grease both to avoid this corrosion and contamination.

Battery Maintenance

An increasing number of sealed battery units are appearing on the market. As can and should be expected, and in line with 'Hutber's Law', he once of *The Daily Telegraph*, any unrequested replacement of existing services and or goods, with the promise of improvements in both, is bound to herald a decrease in efficiency, and quality! Certainly, in the experience of the author, this is so in respect of the introduction of sealed batteries. Fortunately, once the secret of prising off the cleverly concealed tape is grasped, a tape that hides away the individual battery cell filler caps, it is easy enough to proceed as normal and fill with distilled water, as required. Whatever the marketing blurb advises, one of the main reasons for the failure of the few sealed battery units I have owned, was the inability to carry out the latter upkeep.

Nickel-cadmium batteries require little routine care, other than checking the terminal posts are not contaminated, and the cable clamps are secure.

Battery installation on a boat is very important and the following guidelines should be borne in mind:-

Battery Installation

(1) Ensure that the battery is as close as possible to the boat's engine, because:-

 (a) The starting of the engine is the most important function of the battery, as well as the most power-consuming. All starter motors require a lot of current and, where there are high currents, there is a risk of large, unwanted voltage drops. If these occur they will seriously impede the starter motor in its operation. By keeping the battery-to-starter motor wiring as short and heavy as possible, unwanted power loss is minimized.

 (b) The engine is one of the largest causes of electrical noise and interference, on a boat, and, as will be seen later, this can cause problems with electronic equipment. Fortunately, a battery is an excellent medium for absorbing electrical noise and so should be fitted as close as possible to the engine.

(2) As the reliability and capacity of a battery is, more often than not, directly related to the weight of the unit, marine batteries are usually heavier, and thus more awkward to pick up and carry than an automotive unit. It is best not to mount them in small, difficult-to-get-at places. It only increases the chances of an owner incurring a hernia or slipped disc!

(3) Both lead-acid and nickel-cadmium batteries give off hydrogen and oxygen gases, when charging. Hydrogen is a particularly explosive gas and every effort should be made to keep the battery compartment well ventilated, in order to avoid any build-up of gas (Illustration 41).

Illustration Forty One   The Battery Compartment

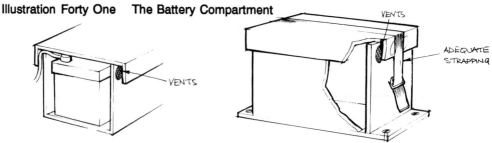

If it is not possible to 'box' the battery, and it is engine compartment based, then a gas and flame-proof electrical fan should be run, whilst charging takes place (Illustration 42). The easiest method of ensuring this, is to wire in the fan to the ignition switch, so it activates when the ignition is turned on. Gas and flame-proof fan's are designed not to produce electrical sparks (from the motor), which could cause hydrogen or engine gases to explode. No switches, solenoids, fuses or relays should be installed in or close to the battery, as they can cause sparking/arcing.

Illustration Forty Two   Venting the Battery

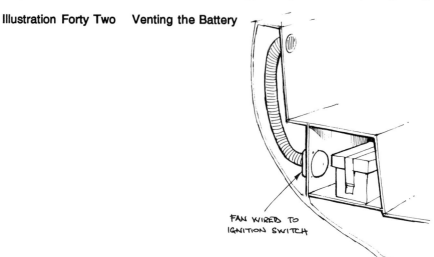

(4) Batteries must be securely fastened in position. It should not be assumed that the weight of a unit will be enough to stop it sliding, or even jumping about. Some thought should be given to the manner in which the craft travels, in order to keep any battery movement to a minimum.

Sailing boats tend to pitch and roll, and spend a lot of the time keeled over. In this case a sensible place to install the battery is as close to the centre line of the craft as is possible, preferably directly above the keel. On the other hand, power boats may well spend a considerable amount of time bouncing about 'on the plane', thus a position within the rear third of the hull is preferable.

No loose metallic objects should be positioned or left anywhere in the vicinity of an uncovered battery. If they are, Murphy's Law will no doubt result in them becoming welded to the battery terminals, when they inadvertently, but inevitably, fall across them. At the best there will be some interesting pyrotechnics, at the worst a fire may result (Illustration 43).

Illustration Forty Three   Battery Terminal Dangers

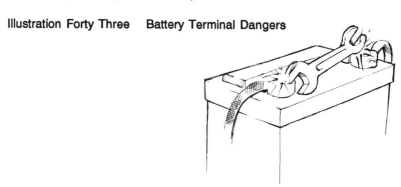

Nowadays the most common means of keeping a battery charged is an Alternator (Illustration 44). This device converts movement energy into electrical energy, using a fraction of the power generated by the boat's engine. An Alternator can also power (almost) any electrical items needed, whilst the engine is running.

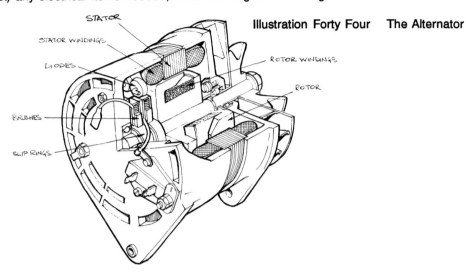

STATOR

STATOR WINDINGS

DIODES

ROTOR WINDINGS

ROTOR

BRUSHES

SLIP RINGS

Illustration Forty Four   The Alternator

When a magnet is passed close to a piece of wire it causes a small current to flow in that wire. The stronger the magnet, or the faster the movement, the more current flows. An Alternator is fitted with an electro-magnet, which to those of us who can remember 'O' Level Physics, is a piece of iron with wire wrapped around it. When a current flows through the wire, named a field winding, a magnetic field is produced. The more current flowing through the field winding, the stronger the magnetic field. If a second winding of wire, known as the stator, is placed around the electro-magnet and the electro-magnet is rotated, then current will flow through the stator winding. The direction of current in the stator depends upon the polarity (north or south) of the magnet. The electro-magnet, like all magnets, has a north and south pole, both of which pass the same piece of wire as it spins. The current in that piece of wire moves, first in one direction and then in the other, resulting in an alternating current (AC), similar to household mains electricity.

Alternators produce an alternating current (AC), from whence it acquires its name. To be of any use, as far as DC circuits are concerned, the alternating current must be made to flow in one direction - it must be converted from AC to DC. This is achieved by a series of diodes, which are basically electrical non-return valves and allow current to flow through them, in one direction, but not the other. By arranging the diodes in a formation often referred to as a Bridge Rectifier, alternating current can be converted into direct current, an action known as Rectification.

Rectification

Having overcome the little matter of 'ironing out' the electrical power direction, there remains the problem associated with the speed at which the electro-magnet rotates. The latter effects the amount of current generated in the stator windings and, as the alternator is directly linked to the engine, usually by a belt, fluctuations in the engine's speed directly results in a change of alternator speed. Consequently, at higher engine revolutions, not only will more power be generated, than is required, but, as a direct result, so will more voltage. If this is allowed to go unchecked, and the voltage rises to 15V, or more, in a 12V system, then damage may result to the battery, and other electrical items.

To overcome this difficulty a clever device has been evolved to control the alternator output voltage, namely a Regulator, or control box. This 'senses' when the voltage at the output of the Regulator, or at the battery terminals, reaches a pre-determined level (Illustration 45). The instrument is a solid state unit, but the principle is the same as used in the old-fashioned dynamo regulator (See Illustration 50).

Regulator

Illustration Forty Five   'Regulation'

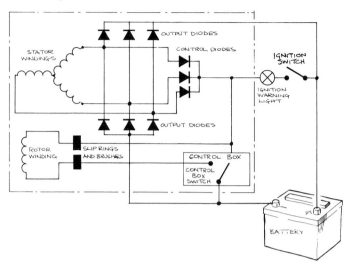

The Regulator upper output level is usually fixed at about 14.5V, at which selected value it cuts off some of the field current. When the field current decreases, so does the magnetic field of the electro-magnet, which, in turn, causes a decrease in the current induced in the stator windings. Thus the voltage decreases at the output of the alternator, and regulation is achieved.

There are two basic types of alternator and Regulator:-

(a) Machine sensed, where the Regulator senses the output and voltage of the alternator internally.

and

(b) Battery sensed, where, an external connection is fitted to the battery or, in the case of multiple battery systems, to the most used battery - usually the general services unit.

It is very important that the type of alternator fitted is matched to the boat's engine. Single battery installations are not so critical, but where more than one has to be taken into account, usually referred to as a split battery installation, the selection of the correct alternator is critical. This consideration is covered in more detail in the relevant section of this chapter.

Since the alternator is a complex electrical item, other than adjustment of the fan-belt, the only maintenance that should be attempted, by the uninitiated, is replacing the brushes. These may be internal or external, and vary in size and type, from manufacturer to manufacturer, but most alternators can be disassembled, allowing internal brushes to be replaced, without much effort. Prior to engaging in this task, it is best to acquire an assembly drawing of the particular unit.

All modern marine engines have alternators fitted, which are matched and geared to the particular power unit. The worst that can happen, if an alternator fails, is that it will have to be replaced. As long as the same type, or a direct equivalent, is fitted, then there can be no problems - apart from paying for the wretched thing! Difficulties may arise, however, if the decision is made to upgrade an alternator's output, perhaps to cope with ever-increasing electrical demands, or to replace an existing dynamo with an alternator.

Alternator Calculations

Either consideration requires calculations and alternator 'knowledge', in order to determine the requisite unit for the job, and how to safely connect it to the particular engine. Referring back to the previously detailed examples in this chapter, for the calculated figures stated, the following procedures should be followed:-

(1) Calculate the battery charge rate (say 10 Ah).

(2) Calculate the maximum current required under normal conditions (say 30 Ah).

(3) Add the battery charge rate to the maximum normal current (in 1 & 2 above) and target an alternator whose average output current is greater than this value.

(4) With a particular unit in mind, study its specification (Illustration 46, Fig A).

Illustration Forty Six   An Alternator Specification

Fig 46A Specification list for a Hitachi LR155-20 alternator, a typical small to medium sized unit.

Model of Alternator	LR155-20
Model of I.C. Regulator	TR1Z-63
Battery Voltage	12V
Nominal Output	12V/55A
Earth Polarity	Negative Earth
Direction of Rotation	Clockwise (Viewed from Pulley End)
Weight	4.3kg (9.5lb)
Rated Speed	5000 RPM
Operating Speed	1000 to 9000 RPM
Speed for 13.5V	1000 RPM or less
Output Current @ 20°C	Over 53A @ 5000 RPM
Regulated Voltage	14.5V ± 0.3V

The particular information of interest, other than output current, is the: *Alternator Characteristics*
(a) Maximum rotation speed, which in this example is 9000 RPM.
(b) Minimum speed, at which the battery is being charged (at about 13.5V). This is given as 1000 RPM or less, and is sometimes referred to as the 'cutting in' speed.
(c) Direction of rotation. In the case of the Hitachi, it is clockwise, when viewed from pulley end.

A performance graph is usually given with the alternator specification (Illustration 46, Fig B), from which it is possible to work out the voltage and current for any engine speed.

Fig 46B

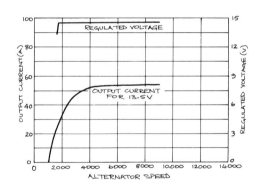

Alternator Performance or Characteristics Graph

(5) Recall from records kept in the log(!) the 'in gear' engine speeds for:
(a) Low speed cruising - say 1250 RPM.
(b) Absolute maximum speed - say 4000 RPM.
(6) Using the figure calculated for maximum current required, in step 3, work out from the graph the engine speed necessary to produce the required current.

In this example:-

The boat engine's RPM at low speed cruising	=	1250 RPM
Boat engine's RPM at absolute maximum speed	=	4000 RPM
Boat's battery charging rate	=	10A
Boat's normal maximum current	=	30A
Total current required	=	40A

From the graph in Illustration 46, Fig B, it will be observed that the alternator develops 40A of current at 2500 RPM. To ensure that the battery will be charged, even when the maximum 'normal' current is being consumed, at low cruising speed, it is best to plan to have the alternator rotating at 2500 RPM, when the engine is turning over at 1250 RPM. This will require a driving pulley ratio of 2:1, so the diameter of the pulley wheel on the engine must be twice the diameter of the alternator pulley (Illustration 47).

Illustration Forty Seven   Alternator/Engine Pulley Ratios

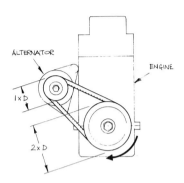

At the same time as the drive pulley ratio has been ascertained (for the minimum engine speed, in order to generate the required current), it must be checked that, when the engine is operating at its maximum speed, the alternator rotates slower than its absolute maximum design speed. Referring back to Illustration 46, Fig B, if the maximum engine speed is 4000 RPM, and the drive pulley ratio is 2:1, then the alternator will rotate at 8000 RPM, well within the designed maximum of 9000 RPM, as set out in Illustration 46, Fig A.

Dynamos

Prior to the 'arrival' of alternators, the Dynamo ruled. They achieved (and still do) the same results as an alternator, in that they generate electrical energy, but in a different manner. Whereas the alternator consists of an electro-magnet rotating within a series of coils of wire that have current induced into them, the Dynamo is of the opposite construction (Illustration 48).

Illustration Forty Eight   The Dynamo

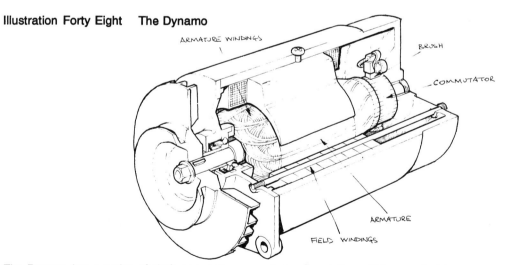

The Dynamo has a series of shaft or armature mounted coils rotating within an electric magnet. The current induced into the coils is passed to the output terminals, via a segmented commutator and a pair of sprung brushes forced against the commutator, the latter 'collecting' the transmitted current. The coils are wired to the commutator segments in such a way that one of the brushes is always connected to the positive ends of the coils, whilst the other brush is always connected to the negative ends. In this manner the output from the Dynamo is constantly DC (direct current) and so no method of rectification (using diodes) is required, as is the case with an alternator.

The major, effective difference between alternators and dynamos is that the latter are unable to rotate at such high speeds, as alternators, because the commutator and armature brush contacts would wear out too quickly. For this reason, dynamo pulleys are usually geared so that the Dynamo rotates at approximately the same speed as the engine (Illustration 49).

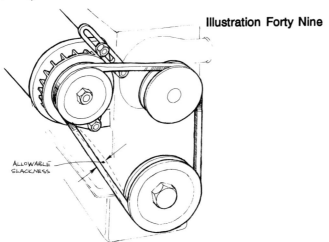

Illustration Forty Nine   Belt Tension

ALLOWABLE
SLACKNESS

If the belt is too loose, then it will slip, with the resultant reduction in the charge rate, and the belt will eventually fall off or break.

This requirement creates the problem that at low engine speeds, such as tick-over, the dynamo is not able to charge the battery. In fact, if the dynamo were directly connected to a battery, at low engine speeds, the battery, rather than being charged, would discharge or 'try to run' into the dynamo. To overcome this shortcoming, a relay is connected to the dynamo output. This relay, or Regulator, only connects the dynamo to the battery when the dynamo output voltage is higher than that of the battery, and charging can take place.

Voltage Regulator & Cut-out

Another problem arises when the engine speed approaches its maximum. At this point the dynamo's output voltage increases to such a degree that, if unchecked, it would damage both the battery and other items connected to the electrical system. Thus a second relay is employed, also connected to the dynamo output. The two relays are normally situated in an external 'control box' - the Voltage Regulator (Illustration 50).

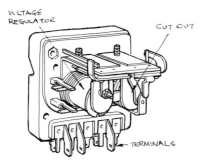

VOLTAGE
REGULATOR

CUT OUT

Illustration Fifty   A Voltage Regulator

TERMINALS

Whilst the dynamo's output voltage is at a safe level (less than approximately 14.5V), the relay connects the field winding of the electric magnet to the dynamo's output. As soon as the voltage rises above 14.5V, the relay energises and disconnects the field winding from the dynamo's output. This causes the electric magnet to weaken, which, in turn, decreases the voltage produced in the armature windings, and hence the output voltage of the dynamo decreases. The output voltage continues to decrease until the relay de-energises and re-connects the field winding to the output, causing the voltage to increase again. This process/cycle repeats itself several times a second and, in so doing, regulates the dynamo output voltage to a maximum 14.5V, even at very high engine speeds.

A third relay is also usually provided which is connected in series with the dynamo output. This senses when too much current is being drawn from the dynamo, disconnecting it from the electrical system. If this current-limiting relay were not fitted, then the unit could be damaged, in the event of a short-circuit in the electrical system.

Fan-Belt

The most necessary item requiring attention is the drive belt, more commonly known as a 'Fan-belt' (due to the automobile connotation). A slack or incorrectly tensioned belt can cause both slippage and wear, with a consequent diminishment in charging efficiency (*See* Illustration 49). Incidentally, this applies equally to the alternator and its drive belt.

*Brushes &
Commutators*

Two other fairly common maintenance matters are worn Brushes and or a dirty/ tarnished Commutator (Illustration 51). Where a dynamo requires refurbishment it will be necessary to strip down the unit. Once 'opened up' it is fairly straightforward to identify the Brushes and the Commutator.

Illustration Fifty One   Dynamo Brushes & Commutator

Fig 51A

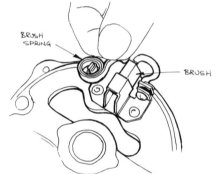

If the brushes are worn unevenly they can be 'trued' up with a strip of sandpaper. This should be wrapped round the radius of the commutator, the smooth face to the commutator, and moved backwards and forwards. They may be so worn down as to require replacing. Broken brush springs will have to be renewed.

Fig 51B

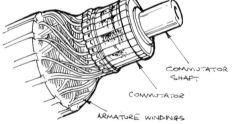

The commutator should be checked and if the copper contacts are simply glazed, they can be lightly cleaned, using a very fine grade of sandpaper (not emery cloth), remembering to scrape out the segment slots with a sharp knife. 'Middlingly' uneven wear of the commutator, usually where the brushes bear down, can be corrected by slipping the armature into a lathe and lightly skimming the commutator. A badly worn commutator will require the purchase of an exchange armature. This might be the right time to replace the dynamo - with an alternator!

**Twin-Battery
Installations**

A Twin-Battery is an excellent step up from a single battery system installation, and not just because 'two are better than one'. A twin-battery system allows one unit to be 'dedicated' to powering the 'domestic' electrical system, whilst the other battery is reserved solely for starting the engine. This arrangement goes a long way to ensuring that a craft's (sole) battery is not accidently discharged, to the point of not having enough 'muscle' to start the engine.

Illustration 52 sketches the simplest twin-battery system.

Illustration Fifty Two   Twin-battery Systems

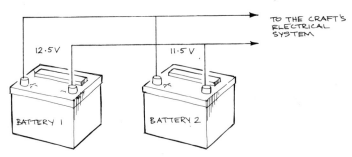

In this arrangement, Battery 1 'passes power' to Battery 2, until the charge in each is equal.

The disadvantage of this basic scheme is that if two batteries are 'joined together, in holy matrimony', well, more literally are connected, and one of them has less charge than the other, then the one battery will discharge into the other, until their respective charges level out. This is an unsatisfactory state of affairs and tends to defeat the object of having two batteries. On the other hand, if they are separately wired, two alternators will be required, one for each battery. Not a very cheap or practical option, for a small craft, but all is not lost!

There are a number of methods of connecting two or more batteries into the electrical system, in such a way as to allow one alternator to charge them all, and yet keep them isolated, so they cannot discharge into one another. The simplest procedure is to fit a Battery Isolator Switch for each battery (Illustration 53).

*Battery
Isolator Switch*

Illustration Fifty Three   Battery Isolator Switches

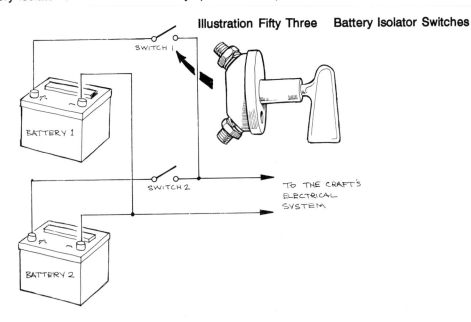

With both Battery Isolator Switches turned off, when it is required to start the engine, turn on one of the switches. Once the engine has started, switch on the other switch, so that both batteries are being charged. When the engine is not running, but domestic power is still required, only turn off the starting battery switch .

A neater and simpler technique is to buy a Combined Battery Select Switch unit. These incorporate the two switches into one assembly (Illustration 54).

*Combined
Battery Switch*

Illustration Fifty Four   Combined Battery Switch

*Possible
Alternator
Switching
Damage*

In any arrangement that relies on manually operated switches, it is important that the alternator is not disconnected from both batteries, whilst the engine is running. This can cause the internal regulator and or diodes of the alternator to be damaged, if there is no load on the alternator output. Some battery select switch units have a field disconnect feature which, if wired to the alternator, disconnects the alternator field winding, thus causing the output of the alternator to turn off, if both batteries are accidently disconnected. Incidentally, this is why, in some installations, the engine has to be stopped, prior to switching off the ignition key.

*Split Charge
Relay*

To save the 'handraulic' aspect of the manual switch, a Split Charge Relay can be fitted in which the relay does the same job as the battery select switch, but automatically (Illustration 55). This system takes 'the chance' out of matters, not allowing the 'luxury' of forgetting to switch both batteries on for charging.

Illustration Fifty Five   Split Charge Relay

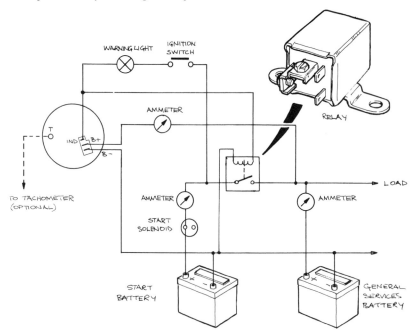

When the ignition switch is operated, the Relay is energised and both batteries are connected to the alternator. As soon as the ignition switch, and thus the engine, is turned off the relay opens and disconnects the starter battery from the general services battery.

Where a Split Charge Relay is fitted, or some sort of manual switch, then it is important that a machine sensed alternator is used. These are set to give an output of 14.2V, and the output sensing takes place internally. This arrangement does have the result that if a large volt drop exists between the alternator and the batteries (say 2V), then they would only receive 12.2V, and would never fully recharge. However, as the switches or relay only have a very low resistance, large volt drops should never occur. But it is a point to bear in mind if a battery appears not be be charging properly. A quick check only requires the use of the meter (*See* Chapter 4 & 11) to ascertain if the resistance is as it should be, that is no higher than 0.1 ohms.

The final method is to fit Blocking Diodes. As was mentioned in the alternator description, a diode is the electrical equivalent of a non-return valve in hydraulic or pneumatic systems (Illustration 56, Fig A). The diode has no moving parts and so is generally more reliable than the split charge relay.

Blocking Diodes

Illustration Fifty Six   Blocking Diode & Heatsink

Fig 56A

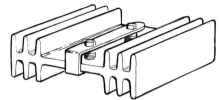

For current to flow the voltage must be greater at the anode than at the cathode. If not, no current will flow through the diode.

The only problem with Blocking Diodes (and diodes) is that, to make current flow, there must be a voltage differential, or drop. This is approximately 0.6V more voltage at the anode than at the cathode, which means that the diode consumes power in relation to the formula:-

Blocking Diode Power Loss

Power (watts) = Voltage(V) x Current (A).

As an example, if 20A of current is passing though the diode to charge the battery, then:-
0.6V x 20A = 12W.

This 12W of power will be inefficiently wasted in the form of heat which, if allowed to build up, can damage the diodes. Accordingly diodes are usually mounted in a Heatsink, in this case a large piece of aluminium with lots of fins, giving a large surface area to dissipate the unwanted heat. (Illustration 56, Fig B).

Heatsink

Fig 56B

Studying the blocking diode circuitry in Illustration 57, it is apparent that, when the alternator is running, a current will flow from the 'A' terminal, through diodes B1 and B2, and charge the two batteries, as well as supplying current to the boat's electrical circuits. When the alternator stops running, the diodes B1 and B2 block the starter battery discharging into the general services battery, or vice-versa.

Illustration Fifty Seven   Blocking Diode Circuit Diagram

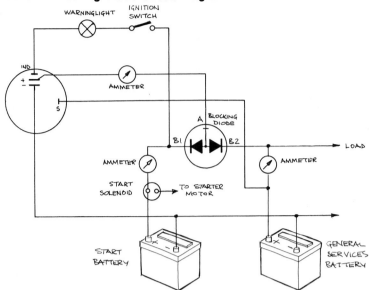

Machine sensed alternators cannot be fitted to a blocking diode system because, as described, for a current to flow through a diode there must be approximately 0.6V voltage drop across the diode, which equates to a 0.6V volt drop in the supply from the alternator to the batteries. If a machine sensed alternator is used, it will provide 14.2V which will drop down to 13.6V. By the time it reaches the batteries (14.2V - 0.6V = 13.6V), the voltage of 13.6V will not be sufficient to fully charge a battery, necessitating the other type of alternator to be used - a battery sensed alternator. These latter units have an external sense connection wired to one of the batteries, generally the most used, domestic services battery. They keep upping their output voltage until they sense 14.2V, at the battery, thus coping with the voltage drop across the Blocking Diodes.

Prior to leaving the subject, there are a couple more considerations to take into account - as if the matter needed even more muddying!

Almost all marine motive power and ancillary supplies are derived from the automotive field. The car battery is designed for the short burst activity of starting the engine and the alternator regulator is set to deliver a maximum voltage of 14.2V, or 2.365V per cell, for a 6 cell battery. Most of the lighting, heating and other vehicle requirements are powered by the alternator, with the engine running, so there is little, or no need for batteries to have any great depth of capacity, nor for the alternator to replace other than a comparatively small amount of discharge.

Deep Cycle Batteries/

In direct contrast, the battery/batteries servicing the domestic supplies of a boat would, ideally, be able to give a reasonable current, over a long period of time. Thus has been 'born' the Deep Cycle Battery, which is able to function efficiently, even at a low state of charge, prior to being charged again. Having designed the Deep Cycle Battery, it was essential to boost the standard alternator output, in order to be able to overcome the increased resistance that takes place within the battery cells, at the very top end of the 'standard' generator output voltage. To this end, it was necessary to 'up' the alternator's output voltage, to keep the current flowing, the required voltage being about 16.5V, or 2.75V per cell, for a 6 cell battery.

External Electronic Voltage Regulator

There are two methods of altering the alternator regulator, one being to replace it! The preferred solution is to fit, in parallel, an External Electronic Voltage Regulator. These units nearly all increase the potential difference across the alternator field windings, causing more current to flow, which, in turn, increases the main output voltage. Hey presto! And do not worry about damaging the alternator, as these minor variations are well within most unit's capacity. It is vital to check with the supplier of any selected 'bolt-on goody', of this type, that it is compatible with the existing alternator, and the battery switching system.

Depending upon the craft and the available space, there are a number of other methods of generating power.

Alternative
Methods of
Generating
Power

Portable
Generators

As their development advances and the units become smaller, quieter and more efficient, so free-standing, self-contained, Portable Generators are becoming increasingly popular. They are usually petrol driven, although diesel and even calor gas powered versions are available, and can deliver 12V/24V DC, as well as 240V AC outputs from 300W to 1500W. Generators giving in excess of 1500W tend not to be so portable, but it is possible to mount them permanently in the engine room. Some form of forced air cooling may be required, such as an electric fan. Inland waterways craft are probably the largest market for these units. This fact can be 'enthusiastically' vouchsafed by anyone woken at 0600hrs, on a Sunday morning, by the thoughtless actions of other boaters in 'kick-starting' their 'genny' into action, at unsociable hours.

There are a considerable choice of different manufacturers and models available. When selecting one, it is worth shopping around, as prices and specifications vary a great deal. The most popular are the petrol driven, 4 stroke, portable units, which tend to be predominantly of Japanese origin. Maybe because of this they are small, efficient, very quiet, reliable, and all look the same! (Illustration 58).

Illustration Fifty Eight   A Portable Generator

With acknowledgements to South Western Marine Factors

The 240V AC mains output from petrol and diesel generators is almost always a true sine wave output, so any equipment that would be used in 'the home' can be 'run' - as long as it doesn't take more power than the generator can provide.

Solar panels are usually made of a thin slice of silicon material that, when exposed to direct sunlight, develops a small voltage of about 0.45V. For solar power to be of any use it must develop 14V, in order to charge the battery. This requirement calls for a large number of individual Solar Panels (or cells) to be wired in series. Practically, this results in their requiring quite a large amount of free deck-space. Various sized panels, with power outputs ranging from 5W to 60W, are available but generally speaking they are not the best method of generating power, as they require quite an expensive initial investment - with comparatively little power output in return!

Those boat owners who do not have the space for solar panels, but who wish to make use of free, natural energy, might consider a Wind Generator. They are similar to alternators and dynamos, in-as-much-as they convert movement energy to electric energy. Once the initial investment has been made, Wind Generators do provide something for nothing, and on a 'pound for watt' basis are probably a cheaper option than solar panels. However the units that develop an acceptable amount of power tend to be quite large and, if they are only to be used when the boat is moored, it will be necessary to find somewhere to store the thing , when not in harness. On the other hand, if a unit is to be a permanent fixture, an owner has to be prepared to put up with a rather unsightly, large propellor mounted 'gizmo' - somewhere. Yet another consideration is the operating noise, which increases with the wind strength. Power output depends on the size of the generator but models are available developing up to about 100W.

Before purchasing a Wind Generator it is important to establish if the power rating quoted is the average, or the peak output. As this depends on the wind speed, a unit that only gives say, 5W of power, in a hurricane, is of little use to 'man, or boat'. It is also worth ascertaining at what wind velocity the generator 'cuts in', and to ensure that this is less than half the average wind speed normally experienced in the relevant area. It is also vital to ensure that it possesses a built-in regulator, in order to keep the output voltage at 12V, irrespective of wind speed. Otherwise the voltage will increase in line with the wind, possibly in excess of the safe limit.

Inverters

Although Inverters don't generate power, as such, they do convert 12V, or 24V, DC into 240V AC. There are a number of different models available and all can 'generate' 240V AC, the important differences being the amount of power, the method used, and the efficiency of the conversion.

Most Inverters are electronic based, converting the 12V DC, from the battery, into a 12V square wave, after which a step-up transformer produces 240V AC. Most Inverters produce a square wave or modified sine wave output (Illustration 59). Only the more expensive models produce true sine wave output, similar to household mains electricity.

Illustration Fifty Nine   Inverter 'Waves'

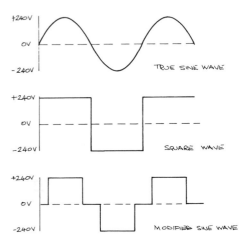

The true, the square, and the modified sine wave output

Where the Inverter produces true sine wave output, there won't be any problems 'driving' household equipment. If, however, an Inverter produces either square or modified sine wave, it is worth checking that particular items can except a non-sine wave voltage. For instance some Hi Fi's, TV's and video's experience audible and visual interference, and certain microwaves cook slower, without a true sine wave input voltage.

Inverter Efficiency

The effectiveness of different makes and models of Inverters varies, but they should all operate in excess of 70% efficiency. Practically, if a particular unit is supplied with 100W of power, then it should not provide less than some 70W of mains power. Once the maximum required AC power has been determined, it is necessary to tot up how much power or current would be drawn, from the battery, at any one time. To calculate this accurately, the efficiency rating for any particular inverter must be determined. As an empirical guide, when considering a 12V system, divide the AC power required by 10 to indicate the DC current required. (For a 24V system, divide by 20).

For example, if the AC power requirement, during an average day (in port?), is as follows:

(a)	Portable colour TV	110W	for 0.3hrs
(b)	Video recorder	40W	for 1.5hrs
(c)	Small iron	450W	for 0.5hr
(d)	Hair dryer	500W	for 0.5hr

Then the total Ampere-hours drain, on a 12V, battery will be:

(110W x 3hrs) + (40W x 1.5hrs) + (450W x 0.5hr) + (500W x 0.5hr) ÷ 10
= 865 ÷ 10 = 86.5 Ah

This represents a considerable battery drain, highlighting the fact that as soon as AC equipment is used, the battery, or batteries, take a hammering.

The peak current requirement, which effects the choice of wire size, can also be calculated, assuming all the equipment is switched on at the same time, as follows

110W + 40W + 450W + 500W = 1100W ÷ 10
= 110A.

This sort of current requirement is approaching that of a small starter motor, so the size and length of cables should be chosen carefully - to avoid unwanted volt drops.

Rotary Converters

As an alternative to an inverter, it is worthwhile considering installing a Rotary Converter. Basically these are a very efficient electric motor, powered from the battery, that 'in-line' drives an alternator to produce 230/240V AC, true sine wave output voltage. Typical power outputs are 500W and 1400W, with the latter giving an intermittent 2000W and surge rating of 3000W. The battery drain current requirement calculations are very similar to those for inverters.

Dual Voltage Alternators

Yet another alternative, is to fit a Dual Voltage Alternator, which can directly replace, or work alongside, the existing engine mounted alternator. Dual Voltage Alternators, as the name implies, have two outputs, one of which is the standard 12V, or 24V, DC output, whilst the other is a 240V AC output, able to provide up to 5KW of mains power. These units are not only much more expensive than the standard alternators, but may require a measure of compromise, as far as the division and distribution of the power is concerned. On the other hand, they do allow mains electricity to be generated, whilst a boat's engine is running, without any worry about replacing large demands on the craft's batteries.

With acknowledgements to South Western Marine Factors

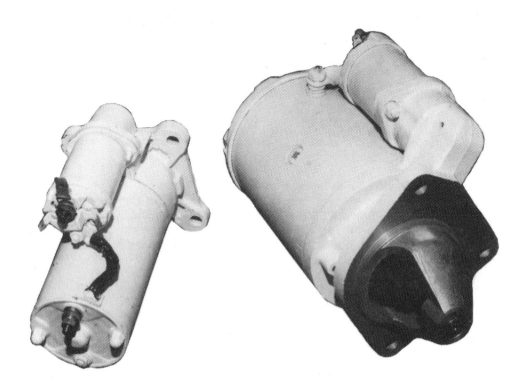

CHAPTER SIX

THE MARINE ENGINE'S NEEDS

Basically three categories of boat engine are installed in boats, namely:-
(a) Inboard diesel units
(b) Inboard petrol units
(c) Outboard engines

From an electrical point of view, there are some items common to all units, which are dealt with first. Components specific to each category are covered in the next section.

Starter Motors

Most engines, other than small outboards, are fitted with electric starting motors. As suggested by their name, they are simply a DC electric motor that commences turning, when electrical power is applied. The Starter Motor must be powerful enough to rotate the particular engine, for the number of revolutions necessary to cause the unit to 'jump into life'. To carry out this task, it must engage the starter ring gear on the flywheel of the engine, before it starts to turn, and then disengage, once the engine 'fires-up'. The distinctive clunking noise, that occurs when the starter switch is switched on, is the pinion teeth 'getting to grips' with the starter ring teeth. (Illustration 60, Fig A)

Illustration Sixty   Starter Motors, Inertia & Pre-engaged

Fig 60A Inertia Starter Motor Engagement

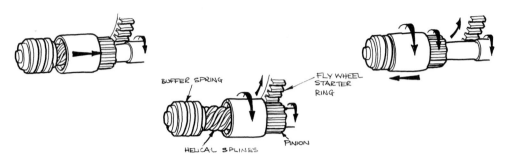

Consideration of the enormous physical power required to perform the required task explains why the Starter Motor is probably the most 'battery draining' item on a boat. Fortunately, in most instances, it only takes a few seconds for an engine to gather its own momentum. Thus the large current demanded by the Starter (between 50A and 500A, depending on the size of unit) is only required for a short period. Unlike an alternator, the Starter Motor is not electrically, or mechanically, connected to the engine, all the time.

Inertia &
Pre-engaged

There are two types of Starter Motor - Inertia and Pre-engaged (Illustration 60, Figs B & C). Both are electrically similar in operation, the differences being in the method of their mechanical engagement with the engine. Pre-engaged Starters have the solenoid 'built-in' (for details of which read on), which makes installation easier, as the starter switch can be directly wired into the Starter. On the other hand they are more expensive than Inertia units.

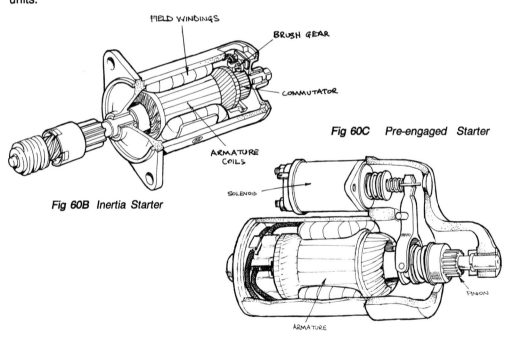

Fig 60B Inertia Starter

Fig 60C   Pre-engaged Starter

The Pre-engaged Starter Motor has a powerful solenoid mounted within it. This not only makes the switched link, between the battery and the Starter Motor, but moves the pinion in and out of engagement with the flywheel starter ring.

Worn Brushes
or a Dirty
Commutator

Starter Motors are generally pretty reliable and robust. If one does go wrong, it is likely to be a mechanical fault, such as a broken brush spring. An associated electrical maintenance problem that can occur is Worn Brushes, and or a Dirty Commutator. The Brushes push against the Commutator, to allow current to pass to the coils on the rotating armature. The Brushes are made of carbon and the commutator is a series of copper plates connected to the armature's coils. As the starter motor gets older, the Brushes tend to wear down, whilst the Commutator becomes glazed, tarnished and dirty.

It is a fairly straightforward job to remove the starter from the engine and cure the problem (Illustration 61). If in doubt, consult the engine's handbook/technical manual for guidelines, and contact the manufacturer of the engine (or the starter motor) for servicing details. If the fault lies in the armature coils or field windings, or is a disintegrating Commutator, then it is best to entrust the unit to specialist hands, or better still - exchange the thing!

Illustration Sixty One   Starter Motor Running Repairs

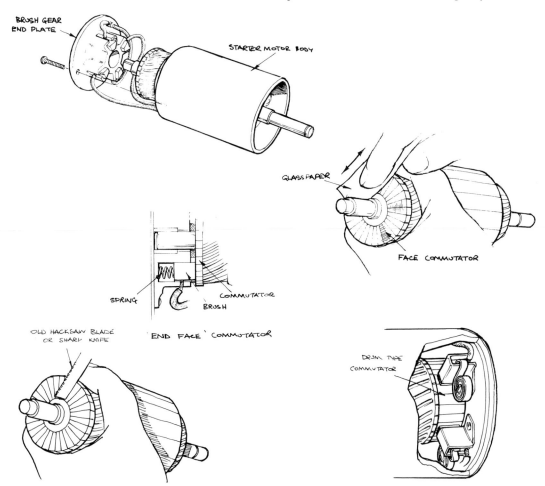

The trick is to:- 1. *Insert a strip of fairly fine emery paper between the commutator and brushes, the abrasive side against the brush. By pulling the emery paper back and forth, not only will the glaze be removed from the face of the brush, but the self-same face will be reshaped to the radius of the commutator. The latter does away with arcing that can happen when single point contact comes about, rather than complete brush-to-commutator contact. 2. The commutator must be 'sanded' to remove any glaze, also following the radius of the commutator, after which the gaps between the commutator segments must be cleaned out with a sharp blade.*

As stated, the starter motor requires a lot of current to force it to turn. When large currents are present there is always the chance of a voltage drop across small resistances, such as switch contacts and thin wires. Most small marine switches can only safely pass a maximum of about 10A of current, before overheating and or arcing occurs. To allow starter motors to be safely activated, a special, heavy-duty relay, or switch, is required - the Solenoid (Illustration 62).

The Solenoid

Illustration Sixty Two   The Solenoid

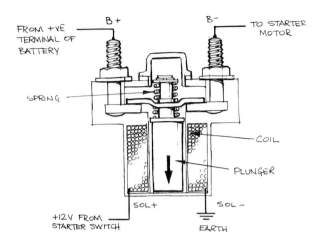

The battery's +ve terminal is connected to the B+ terminal of the Solenoid and the B- terminal is taken to the +ve terminal of the Starter Motor. The two other terminals, SOL+ and SOL- are, respectively, taken to the starter switch and battery -ve terminal (0V).

Under normal conditions, the 'T' shaped, metallic plunger is kept away from the B+ and B- terminals by a spring. However, when the ignition switch is activated, 12V is applied to the SOL+ terminal, which occasions a current to flow through the Solenoid's coil, causing a magnetic field to be set-up. This pulls the metallic plunger downwards, connecting the B+ and B- terminals, thus providing a path for the (heavy) current to flow directly from the battery to the starter motor. Once the engine has 'fired into life', the starter switch is switched off, disconnecting the +12V from the Solenoid's coil, thus the magnetic field collapses, no longer pulling the plunger downwards. The spring forces the plunger upwards, breaking the B+ and B- connection, cutting off the current and turning off the starter motor.

Starter Motor Electrical Circuits

Illustration 63 sketches a typical starter motor electrical circuit.

Illustration Sixty Three   A Typical Starter Motor Electrical Circuit

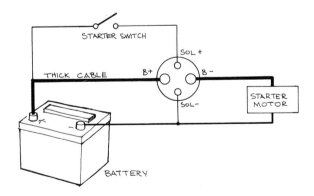

It will be noted that the cable taking the large current (required for the starter motor) is shown as bold, and labelled 'thick cable'. This is to emphasise the fact that the wiring must be of a sufficiently heavy gauge cable, with a large-enough-diameter to carry the current required, without dropping too much voltage.

The size of voltage drop hinges on the resistance of the cable and the current flowing through it. The resistance of the cable depends on the diameter of the wire, and its length. Therefore, in starter motor circuits, and for that matter any other circuit carrying large currents, the thickest cable possible is utilised, and the wiring kept as short as is possible. Note that cabling and the choice is detailed in Chapter 7.

Once the engine is running, it is important that information about the unit's performance and efficiency is available. Apart from peace of mind, this enables any fault to be spotted and preventative maintenance carried out, thus avoiding costly and or dangerous major mechanical failure. Most marine engines are supplied with some instrumentation and it is very useful to know how the various items work, so that they can be checked, or replaced, if faulty. Understanding also facilitates fitting further Engine Monitoring equipment, if and when required. Basically, all engine instruments consist of a sensor, usually located on or by the power unit, and a display. The latter is almost always an analogue, moving coil meter, although digital versions are becoming increasingly common. The display will have +12V and 0V connections, providing power to the display, as well as the bulb used to illuminate it, for night-time use.

Engine Monitoring

Sensors come in three types:-

Sensors

(a) Critical Point. The simplest type and basically a switch, controlled by the status of the item being monitored. Whilst the item is satisfactory, the switch stays open but if it reaches a critical point the switch closes. This type of Sensor is often used for monitoring oil pressure, coolant temperature and battery charging. (Illustration 64, Fig A).

Illustration Sixty Four   Sensors

Fig 64A   Critical Point Sensor

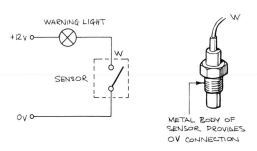

The sensor can be wired in series to a warning light or, if preferred, a 12V buzzer. When the critical point is reached, and the switch closes, the warning light illuminates, or the buzzer sounds.

(b) Continuous. These provide a continuous signal to the display, showing the state of the item being monitored. They are basically a variable resistor, in which the resistance changes, as the status of the item alters, and are often deployed for monitoring most of the temperature, pressure and position related engine data (Illustration 64, Fig B)

Fig 64B   Continuous Sensor

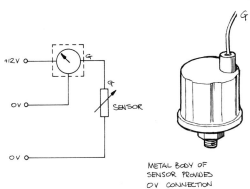

(c) Combined. These instruments combine Critical point and Continuous Sensors into one unit, possessing the best of each but, understandably, are more expensive (Illustration 64, Figs C & D).

Fig 64C Combined Sensor

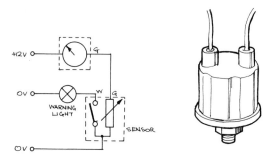

Fig 64D

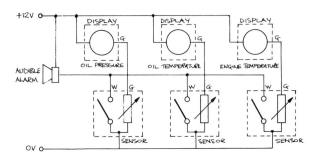

In this imaginary, integrated system (Fig D), each display is wired separately to its Sensor, indicating only the status of the item it is monitoring. By connecting the 'W' terminals, in parallel, a very neat and effective warning system is created. With the 'W' connections (of all the Sensors) wired in parallel, and connected to the audible alarm, if the oil pressure, oil temperature or engine temperature should reach a critical condition, then the relevant switch closes. This allows current to flow from the +12V supply, through the alarm, via the relevant switch, to 0V, causing the alarm to sound a warning, thus indicating there is a problem. The root-cause can then be ascertained by inspecting the displays, to see which item has become critical.

Sensor Technical Information

All the aforementioned sensors are quite easy to test, but some Technical Information will be required. This may be included in the engine service manual or instructions, but if not, a telephone call to the engine or instrument manufacturer might(?) provide the answers. Information that could be required includes the state (temperature, pressure) at which the critical point instrument switches, or the typical resistance values for continuous sensors, at various states. Armed with these facts, an electrical meter can be used to test the resistance of continuous sensors or indicate if a critical point sensor has switched or not. Some examples of fault-finding are detailed in Chapter 11.

The instruments detailed cover nearly all the engine monitoring systems used, however four other types employ different sensors. They are :-

Tachometer

(a) The Tachometer. This monitors the engine speed (revolutions per minute, or RPM).

Tachometer Pulses

The sensor comes in many different guises, but in all of them it provides a number of electrical Pulses to the instrument/display. The number of Pulses received will either match the engine revolutions, or be a multiple of those revolutions (two, three or four times the number of engine revolutions). The instrument counts the number of Pulses, calculates the engine speed, and displays the value on a meter (Illustration 65).

Illustration Sixty Five   Tachometer Pulses

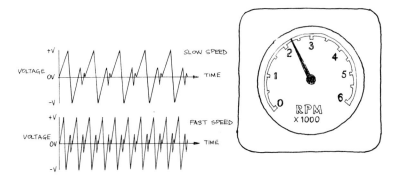

Where the power unit is a petrol engine, it is normal practice for the Tachometer sensor to be connected to the high tension output of the ignition coil, the low tension input to the coil, or even one of the coils of the magneto (Illustration 66).

Petrol Engine Tachometers

Illustration Sixty Six   Petrol Engine Tachometer Connections

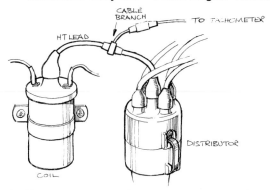

In this case the Tachometer sensor is connected to the HT lead from the ignition coil.

Diesel Engine Tachometers

Diesel engines don't have a 'convenient' electrical ignition system, so it is difficult to locate an electrical pulse whose frequency is related to the engine speed. To overcome this 'tiresome' fact, a common method is to tap into the unrectified output of the alternator, where and if an external regulator is fitted. However, this is not possible on a number of alternators, in which case an inductive or generator type sensor is used. Inductive sensors pick up pulses from a special timing disc attached to the flywheel, or the starter ring gear teeth. Generator sensors consist of a shaft directly connected to the camshaft, with a permanent magnet attached. A coil of wire surrounds the magnet so that the rotation of the camshaft, causes the sensor's shaft to turn, the magnet rotates and generates small pulses of current in the surrounding coils, which are transmitted to the Tachometer.

At slow engine speeds the pulses from these various sensors are just about visible on analogue meters. They show up as a jittering movement in the needle, when measuring DC voltage, and so sensors can, to some degree, be checked. Alternatively it is possible to measure the pulses with the meter set to AC volts. A slight voltage should be visible which rises in line with an increase in engine speed. Note that different sensors may require different methods of testing. It is thus necessary to experiment with the DC and AC voltage ranges of a meter, until some indication that the sensor is working is observed.

(b) The Engine Hour Meter. An often underestimated item but useful for keeping track of when routine engine maintenance, or servicing, is due, and invaluable for calculating an engine's fuel consumption. The Meter does not have a sensor, simply a connection on the back of the instrument that is wired to the ignition switch, or the field

Engine Hour Meters

winding of the alternator. When the engine is started, + 12V is applied to this connection and the Engine Hour Meter starts timing. As soon as the engine stops, the + 12V is removed, and the meter stops running.

Battery Voltmeter

(c) The Voltmeter (Illustration 67). This instrument is used to monitor the state of the the battery, when the engine is 'off', and the state of the battery charging system, when the engine is running. Voltmeters are usually connected either across the battery (in a split battery system, it would be across the general services battery) or across the + 12V and 0V connections in the main distribution/fuse box. Most + 12V Voltmeters have a scale marked from + 8V to + 16V, whilst + 24V Voltmeters range from + 18V to + 32V. Nearly all have coloured bands, with the green zone indicating that the battery is fully charged, and the charging system is in order; the red zone flagging that the charging system is producing too high a voltage, and could well cause damage to the battery, if not rectified quickly; and the red striped zone demonstrating that the battery requires charging.

Illustration Sixty Seven   Battery Voltmeter

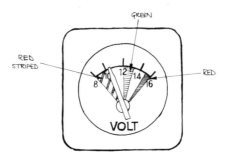

The Voltmeter on a correctly functioning electrical system should:- drop to as low as + 8V, when the engine is started; rise rapidly to + 10V, or more, when the starter switch is released; after a few minutes it should reach + 11V, after twenty to thirty minutes + 12V, and after 1 to 2 hours it should be positioned at its 'stable at rest' voltage, which, for a fully charged battery, is about + 12.7V*; during charging the voltage should be about 13.7V to 14.2V - much higher and battery damage could occur*.

*These upper voltage readings are greater where deep cycle batteries are fitted. See Chapter 5.

Ammeter

(d) The Ammeter (Illustration 68). This instrument measures the current flowing from the engine's generator to the battery, when the engine is running, and the discharge current from the battery to the boat's electrical system, when the engine is switched off. As the Ammeter is measuring current it must have a special sensor, called a shunt. This is connected into the circuit in series, so that all the circuit's current flows through this shunt.

Illustration Sixty Eight   The Ammeter

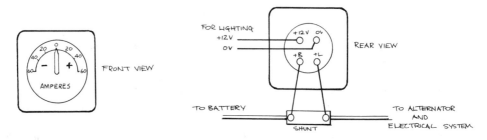

The shunt has a very low, known value of resistance. As the current flows through it, a tiny voltage is dropped across it, which is measured by the Ammeter. As the voltage is proportional to the amount of current, the Ammeter can measure how much current is flowing. If this is flowing

from the battery to the rest of the electrical system (discharging), the meter's needle moves to the left-hand side, showing a negative current. If the current flows from the generator to the battery (charging), the meter's needle moves to the right-hand side, indicating a positive current.
Where more than one battery is deployed, it is well worth considering fitting an ammeter, and voltmeter, to measure each one.

Starter motors and engine monitoring instruments are the only electrical items common to both diesel and Petrol Engines, apart from the generating equipment. In fact, diesel engines require no other electrical items to function.

Petrol Engines

Ignition System

On the other hand, Petrol Engines must have an Ignition System, in order to produce an electrical spark to effect the combustion cycle. This arrangement is identical, in principle, to that fitted to the motor car engine, but is marinised. The Ignition System must ignite the petrol mixture, in the combustion chamber, during the particular cylinder's compression cycle. For the Ignition System to work correctly, and to ignite the fuel mixture, a spark of between 4,000V and 10,000V is necessary, generated at the correct time in each of the engine's combustion strokes. Basically, the reason a diesel engine does not require an Ignition System is that their combustion is caused by squirting the fuel, under pressure, into the cylinder, at the appropriate point of the combustion stroke. The ignition 'bang' is compression, not electrically induced.

Prior to fleshing out a modern-day ignition system, fitted with a distributor, it may not be remiss to sketch the 'power-house' of petrol engines, in 'the old days', namely the Magneto (Illustration 69).

Magneto Ignition

Illustration Sixty Nine   The Magneto

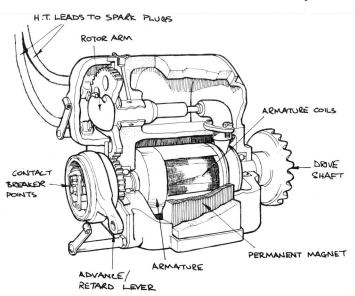

The Magneto was directly linked to the engine. It consisted of an armature, with a series of coils wound round it, that rotated within a large, permanent magnet. As soon as the engine started to turn, by means of an electric, or 'handraulic', starter, a large voltage was induced in the armature coils. This could be switched to each of the sparking plugs, at the correct time, by the integral contact breaker points, and rotor arm, fitted within a distributor cap. (For details of the technicalities, follow the description of the modern-day coil ignition system).

Most problems experienced with petrol engines are due to a defective ignition system, thus a concise understanding is vital. To facilitate this, Illustration 70 is a simple diagram sketching the four basic 'building blocks' of an ignition system - the engine timing sensor (Block A), the coil (Block B), the distributor (Block C), and the sparking plugs (Block D), with an explanatory notation.

Illustration Seventy   The Petrol Engine Ignition System

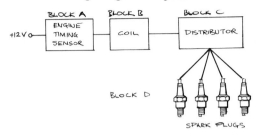

A typical Ignition System for a four cylinder petrol engine. Block 'A' is the engine timing sensor, that monitors the engine for the optimum time to ignite the petrol mixture in a particular cylinder. When it judges the time is right, it disconnects the +12V from the input to the coil (Block B). This action causes a very short, but very high voltage spark, or pulse, to be discharged by the coil, which is routed into the distributor (Block C). The distributor's task is to make sure that the pulse is passed to the correct sparking plug to be ignited, at any particular time in the engine's cycle, achieving this by switching extremely quickly between the engine's sparking plugs.

Engine Timing Sensor (Block A)

Until a few years ago the traditional, well-proven and time-tested method of achieving the Engine Timing (sensor) function was to employ a mechanical device - 'Contact Breaker Points' (Illustration 71).

Illustration Seventy One   The Distributor & Contact Breaker Points

Fig 71A   A Distributor

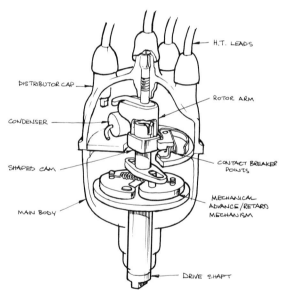

The illustration sketches a typical automotive engine distributor. The shaft, which has a shaped cam, rotates at the same speed as the engine, and is often gear-driven off the camshaft. The cam forces the moving contact away from the fixed contact, and then allows them to remake contact.

   Note that the cam sketched (Fig B), is for a four cylinder engine, and thus has four sides, which allow the contacts to make and break four times, for every complete rotation of the shaft. If a voltage is applied to the fixed contact, then whenever the contacts close, current flows through the contact points, and whenever they open, current stops flowing. In effect the contact breaker points are a mechanical switch, which opens and closes in time with the engine's rotation.

Contact Breaker Points

The problem with Contact Breaker Points is that, being mechanical in operation, they:-
(a) Can work loose, allowing the gap between the points to vary, which, in turn, leads to poor contact and performance.
(b) Allow 'wear and tear', which effects performance.

(c) Are subject to arcing, which causes the points to become pitted and burnt, occasioning poor contact.

All these faults effect the timing. To decrease the possibility of arcing, a condenser is connected across the points. The condenser is basically a capacitor. It absorbs sudden changes in voltage, or current flow, and as arcing is the result of both these factors, the condenser helps to stop it occurring The traditional position for the Contact Breaker Points is inside the distributor cap. The Points require checking fairly reguarly and, as they are relatively inexpensive and prone to mechanical wear, it is worth changing them, whenever the engine is serviced (Illustration 71, Fig B).

Fig 71B *Contact Breaker Points*

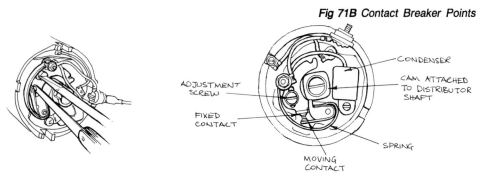

To check and adjust the Contact Breaker Points requires a set of feeler gauges. First loosen the adjustment screw and open the points, as wide as possible. Check that both contacts are smooth and clean. Then turn the engine over, by using a spanner to turn either the crankshaft pulley nut, or the alternator pulley nut (whilst pressing hard down on the fan-belt). Remember that it is easier to turn over an engine with the sparking plugs removed, which does away with the restraints of compression. With the points at their maximum opening, stop turning the engine and set the gap to the engine manufacturer's recommendation, using the feeler gauges.

In comparatively recent years, a number of different electrical methods of achieving the same result as contact breaker points have been developed, without being prone to mechanical wear. Illustration 72 sketches an Inductive Coil Sensor, now fitted to many modern petrol engines, to sense the engine timing.

Inductive Coil

Illustration Seventy Two   Inductive Coil Sensor

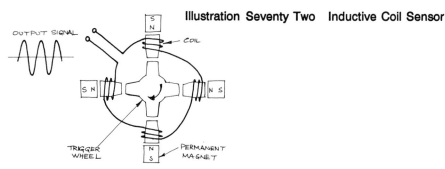

As the engine rotates, so does the trigger wheel. A four cylinder engine has four arms, and four permanent magnets, whilst a six cylinder unit possesses six arms, and six permanent magnets. The arms, being metallic, divert the magnetic fields of each of the permanent magnets, as they pass by. This deflection of the magnetic fields causes a small current to flow, in each of the coils. These currents combine to result in a signal being generated at the output, used to 'tell' the engine's timing.

The 'Hall Effect' Sensor (Illustration 73) is quite a new development, even by modern-day electronic ignition standards. It owes its function to the discovery that when a current flows through some semi-conductor materials (such as indium arsenide), and a magnetic field is placed adjacent to it, the voltage across the material changes. This effect allows relatively cheap sensors to be produced. If a permanent magnet is attached to the distributor shaft, one of these sensors can be used to deduct the engine's timing.

'Hall Effect' Sensor

Illustration Seventy Three   'Hall Effect' Sensor

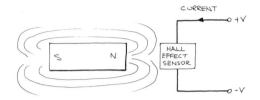

Both Inductive Coil and 'Hall Effect' Sensors are, more often than not, mounted on the outside of the distributor, which allows easy removal, in case of failure. Neither ordinarily require adjustment - they work perfectly, or not at all! It is perhaps unfortunate that as electronic systems become more sophisticated, they also become harder to fault-find, and repair. Professional help or part replacement is usually required. The two electronic sensors are always used in conjunction with an amplifier unit that receives the timing signal produced and, using some form of transistor circuit, magnifies the signal, so that it can provide the coil with a large current, for the primary windings.

Incidentally, an equivalent amplifier unit that works with contact breaker points is available, and various makes can be purchased from accessory shops. They work by reducing the amount of current which the points have to switch, thus decreasing arcing and increasing the life of the points. By amplifying the signal from the points, as they close, a larger current can be made to flow into the coil, than would normally be possible, if only points were fitted. This larger current results in a higher voltage output, and a 'fatter' spark at the sparking plugs.

The Coil
(Block B)

A typical petrol engine Coil (Illustration 74, Fig A) is, simply no more than a transformer (Illustration 74, Fig B). Transformers can convert (or transform) a small voltage into a large one (as in this case), or a large voltage into a small one. As 'nothing is for something', the conversion of a small to large voltage results in a reduced output current, whilst the large to small voltage transformation increases the output current.

Illustration Seventy Four   The Coil

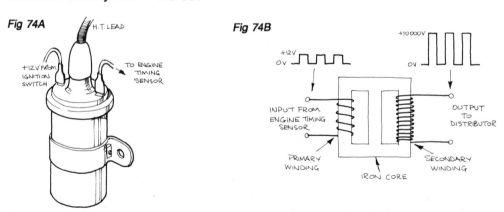

Basically a transformer consists of a ferrite (iron) core, around which are wound two coils of wire, usually referred to as the primary and secondary windings. The number of turns of wire, in each winding, determines whether the unit will transform a small to a large voltage, or vice-versa. The input voltage, to be transformed, is always applied to the primary winding, whilst the transformed output voltage is always taken from the secondary winding. If the primary winding has more turns of wire, than the secondary, then the output voltage will be smaller than the input voltage. Where the primary winding has less turns of wire, than the secondary, then the output voltage will be bigger than the input voltage - as is the case of the High Tension Coil of a petrol internal combustion engine.

Illustration 75 sketches the schematic layout of a petrol engine Ignition Circuit. When the ignition switch is closed +12V is connected to the engine timing sensor.

Simple Ignition Circuit

Illustration Seventy Five   A Simple Ignition Circuit

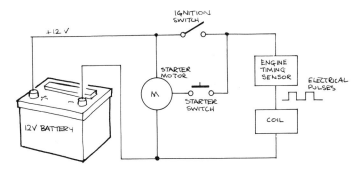

The timing sensor detects when one of the engine's cylinders should receive a high voltage spark, in order to ignite the petrol mix. Prior to the spark being produced, +12V is applied to the coil's primary (low voltage) winding. As the +12V is applied, current flows through the primary winding, causing a magnetic field to build up across the winding. The engine timing sensor only applies the +12V to the coil, for a short period, and then disconnects the +12V, at the moment the spark is to be produced. The current thus ceases to flow through the primary winding, with the result that the magnetic field across the winding cannot exist, and quickly dies away. When a magnetic field decreases (or for that matter increases) it has an effect on any surrounding electrical wires, inducing a voltage across them. In practice this results in a voltage being produced across the secondary winding. The latter is very close to the primary winding, and is wound on the same iron core, which helps improve the passing of voltage to the secondary winding. As the coil's secondary winding has a much larger number of turns of wire, than its primary winding, this induced voltage is considerably larger than the input voltage (which in this example is +12V). If the battery is in reasonable condition, and the ignition system is working properly, this voltage may be of the magnitude of 4,000V to 20,000V.

Coils are normally pretty reliable but, none-the-less can 'burn-out', or develop a partial short, which results in a decrease in the output voltage. It is possible to check both the primary and secondary windings with a meter, set to resistance. Generally speaking the primary winding should be less than 3 ohms, and the secondary winding between 2.5k ohms and 10k ohms. More accurate values may be available from the engine manufacturer, but readings within these values should indicate a coil is in 'reasonable health'.

The Distributor (Illustration 76) is a distinctive, if universal appendage on all petrol engines. Its job is to connect the high voltage spark to the appropriate cylinder requiring ignition. The Distributor is basically a very fast rotating, multi-position switch. Each 'station' represents the point of connection to one of the engine's cylinders. Each time the rotor arm passes one of these stations, an electrical connection is very briefly made, and a high voltage charge is routed to the relevant sparking plug, via the high tension leads.

The Distributor (Block C)

Illustration Seventy Six   The Distributor & Suppressors

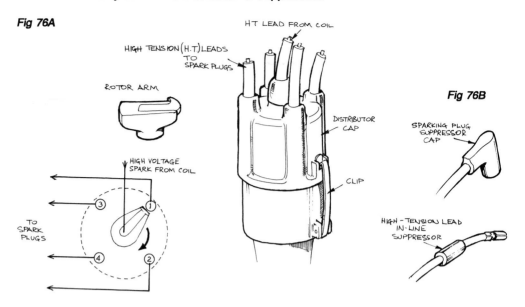

Fig 76A

HT LEAD FROM COIL

HIGH TENSION (H.T.) LEADS TO SPARK PLUGS

ROTOR ARM

DISTRIBUTOR CAP

HIGH VOLTAGE SPARK FROM COIL

TO SPARK PLUGS

CLIP

Fig 76B

SPARKING PLUG SUPPRESSOR CAP

HIGH-TENSION LEAD IN-LINE SUPPRESSOR

The rotor arm sits on top of an engine drive shaft inside the Distributor cap. As the name suggests, the rotor arm rotates, all but touching a number of fixed contacts located inside the Distributor Cap, as it whirls round, passing a spark to each one. As it spins at the same speed as the engine, and each spark is 10,000V, or so, the rotary arm and the contacts are prone to mechanical wear, and should be checked at regular intervals. Both the cap and the rotor arm are reasonably inexpensive and easy to replace, so if their condition is in any doubt, change them, more especially as old or damaged units can seriously effect an engine's performance. Due to the high voltages present in the Distributor and high tension (HT) leads, it is easy for the ignition spark to incorrectly route, thus it is vital to ensure that both are dry and clean, as well as free from oil and dirt. The presence and combination of damp and dirt can easily provide a 'highly desirable' alternative path to earth, decreasing the strength of the ignition voltage at the sparking plug.

To clean the Distributor cap and HT leads, thoroughly wash them in a bucket of hot, soapy water. To dry, place them in an oven, at the lowest setting, for 15 minutes or so, thus ensuring they are completely dry. Proprietary anti-moisture, silicone sprays, such as WD 40, should only be used to treat an engine's electrics, if the system is already moisture-laden, and will not start. These products are good as a short-term measure, but if they are used often, may attract dirt and oil, which if not cleaned away, will create further problems.

An excellent method of tracing high tension 'leaks' is to inspect the distributor cap and leads in the dark, with the engine running. In the dark? Yes, for that is when the errant flashes and sparks show up best of all.

Another source of high tension problems are suppressors. They are often fitted to damp down the adverse effect that ignition system sparks have on nearby radios, or television sets. (All of us must have suffered the wretched nuisance of a passing car obliterating a 'dearly wished to be heard' commentary, or programme). Suppressors are most often inserted in the HT leads, or are an integral part of the sparking plug cap, (Illustration 76, Fig B).

Sparking Plugs (Block D)

The sole job of the Sparking Plug (Illustration 77) is to convert the high voltage pulse, from the distributor, into a spark, with which to ignite the fuel mixture in the cylinder. The body of the Sparking Plug is the -ve (0V) terminal, which is connected, through the engine block, to the negative side of the ignition circuit. The +ve, high voltage (high tension) supply is connected to the top of the 'Spark' Plug. The positive and negative supplies are very close together at the 'working end' of the Plug, so close that the approximate 10,000V difference between the two electrodes causes the current to 'jump' the gap, in the form of a spark. Sparking Plugs should be serviced regularly (Illustration 77, Fig B)

Illustration Seventy Seven   The Sparking Plug

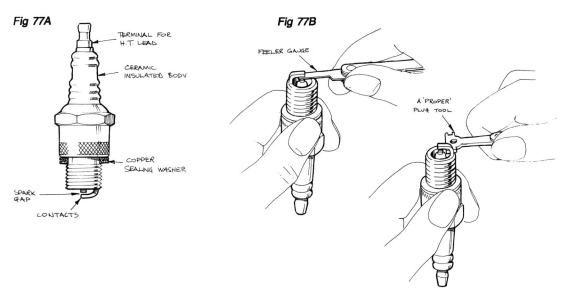

Fig 77A

TERMINAL FOR H.T. LEAD

CERAMIC INSULATED BODY

COPPER SEALING WASHER

SPARK GAP

CONTACTS

Fig 77B

FEELER GAUGE

A 'PROPER' PLUG TOOL

The aperture between the electrodes is quite critical and should be checked at regular intervals. Plugs are manufactured to various ratings and specifications, and require varying gaps. In general, these range between 20 thou' (0.020 in/0.50mm) and 40 thou (0.040 in/1.0mm). If in doubt consult the relevant handbook, to ascertain the correct gap size.

To set a sparking plug electrode gap,using a set of feeler gauges:-
(a) Select the correct thickness feeler blade, for the required gap, and attempt to slide it into the space. If the feeler gauge cannot be inserted (without using any force) or, alternatively, if it is possible to wobble the blade about, then it will be necessary to adjust the gap accordingly.
(b) Where the gap is too small, gently ease open the earth electrode, using a thin bladed screwdriver, if the 'proper' tool is not available. Re-check the setting with the feeler gauge.
(c) If the gap is too large, gently tap the earth electrode against a solid object, and recheck.
(d) Repeat (b) or (c), until the gap is correct.

Marine Sparking Plugs should be replaced approximately every 500 hours of engine use, or annually, whichever is the soonest. It is important to ensure that replacements are of the recommended type, as incorrect ones can cause extensive engine damage – especially where overlong (Illustration 78).

Illustration Seventy Eight   Incorrect Sparking Plugs

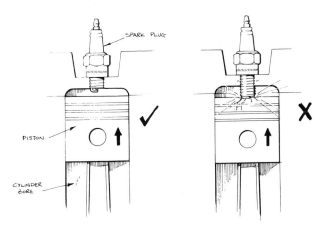

SPARK PLUG

PISTON

CYLINDER BORE

*Timing the
Engine*

As detailed, all the separate 'building blocks' of an ignition system must work and fit together. For the whole to operate to its optimum performance, the setting, or timing, of the arrangement has to be correct. The optimum moment for the spark to be produced, in a cylinder bore, is immediately prior to the piston reaching the top of its stroke. This juxtaposition allows for the short time it takes the spark to ignite all the combustible mixture, and produce full power (Illustration 79, Fig A). If the spark ignites too early in the piston's upward stroke, the fuel will burn too soon, effectively trying to turn the piston back from its upward progress. This pre-ignition, also known as 'pinking', can often be heard as a distinctive pinging/tinkling noise (Illustration 79, Fig B). If the spark ignites too late in the cycle, when the piston is on its way back down the cylinder, known as retarded ignition, then too much of the explosion's thrust will be lost (Illustration 79, Fig C).

Illustration Seventy Nine   Optimum, Pre & Retarded Ignition

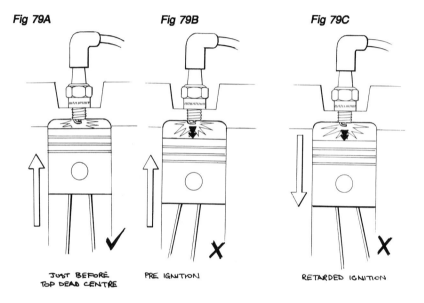

Fig 79A   *Fig 79B*   *Fig 79C*

JUST BEFORE TOP DEAD CENTRE   PRE IGNITION   RETARDED IGNITION

Timing Marks

There are a number of methods of checking the timing of an engine's ignition. Most units have Timing Marks stamped on the crankshaft pulley, or flywheel, and the adjacent engine block. In fact, there are usually two marks! One indicates Top Dead Centre (TDC) and the other, the actual Timing Mark, some 5° before TDC (Illustration 80).

Illustration Eighty   Timing Marks

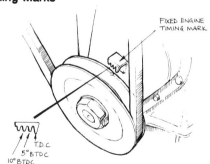

FIXED ENGINE TIMING MARK

TDC
5° BTDC
10° BTDC

Usually from the handbook, ascertain the engine speed at which the timing should be set, and the location of the relevant timing marks. At the designated engine speed (normally tick-over or slightly faster), the fixed engine and 5° before TDC marks should be aligned, to ensure the correct position for the 'generation' of the ignition spark for the No. 1 cylinder. The handbook will also detail the correct 'firing order', that is the order in which the high tension leads must be routed from the distributor cap to the individual sparking plugs.

A number of methods are available to check, set, or reposition the ignition timing:-

Method 1. The modern way is to employ a stroboscopic timing light ('Strobe') and a tachometer. A 'Strobe' is a totally accurate means of ascertaining if the timing marks are in or out of alignment, and thus if the timing is correctly or incorrectly set, whilst the engine is running (Illustration 81, Fig A).

Methods of Timing

The 'Strobe'

Illustration Eighty One   Checking The Timing

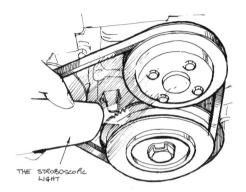

Fig 81A

(a) Referring to the tachometer, set the engine to the recommended speed.

(b) Connect the 'Strobe' to the No. 1 cylinder sparking plug - almost always the first cylinder back from the front of the engine. The 'Strobe' produces a very bright and short flash of light, every time an ignition spark is produced at the sparking plug end of the HT lead.

(c) Aim the 'Strobe' at the timing marks. As it only flashes once every engine revolution, it gives the human eye the impression that the timing marks are stationary. Beware of catching clothing, or fingers, in the engine's rotating bits and pieces.

Method 2. Prior to the 'strobe' there was the other way... Static setting. Line up the timing marks, loosen the distributor clamp, turn the distributor back a quarter turn, the opposite way to the usual rotation, prior to advancing it until the points just start to open. Then re-tighten the clamp (Illustration 81, Fig B). The reason for 'backing up' the distributor is to take any (inevitable) backlash out of the mechanical components, when winding the distributor body forward.

The 'Old Way'

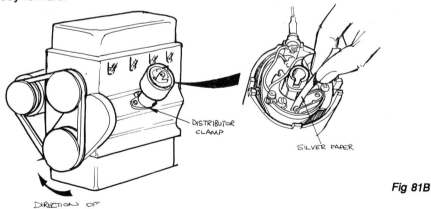

Fig 81B

(a) Rotate the engine by hand, so the distributor points are wide open and place a slip of silver cigarette paper between them.

(b) Continue to rotate the engine by hand in the correct direction, that is the rotation that the crankshaft turns when running - almost always clockwise (Facing the front of the engine).

(c) When the timing marks line up, the points should just be opening. This is indicated by the slither of silver paper being able to be withdrawn, from the 'grip' of the points, which is the exact moment at which the spark would flash across the electrodes of the sparking plug.

Outboard
Engines

Outboard Engines are, for all intents and purposes, all petrol driven. The smaller, low power units are generally two-stroke, while the larger units are more often four-stroke engines. Being petrol driven, they are fitted with an ignition system. On the bigger Outboard Motors, this is very similar to that of the previously described inboard engines, whilst the ignition system of the smaller units is often a magneto or a capacitor discharge (CD) type system.

*The Flywheel
Magneto*

These circular Flywheel Magnetos are basically an ignition coil placed very close to a permanent magnet, attached to the inside of the engine's flywheel (Illustration 82, Fig A)

Illustration Eighty Two   The Flywheel Magneto

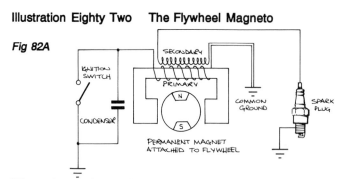

Fig 82A

When the engine is being manually started, the flywheel is spun round and a current induced into the primary winding, creating a magnetic field. The contact breaker is timed so that it opens, whilst current flow is at its maximum. As soon as this occurs, all current stops flowing and the magnetic field collapses. This latter development causes a very large voltage to be produced across the secondary winding, big enough to generate a spark at the sparking plug. The magneto requires no external battery to power the coil, as all the energy required to 'fire' the spark is generated by the spinning of the permanent magnet past the coil.

Once the engine is running, the permanent magnet continues to spin and the required ignition sparks continue to be generated. In fact, to stop the engine it is necessary to 'short' out this stream of HT voltage... otherwise the unit will run on until the fuel tank is exhausted!

Most outboard engines have one or more additional coils, also placed close to the magnet. The power induced into these can be used to keep a small capacity battery charged. The voltage produced is usually about 28V AC, which is, more often than not, rectified and regulated down to 12V DC. This rather crude, small outboard power generation is usually limited to about 50W. With this in mind, it is important not to overload a system by making too many electrical demands. Additionally, these simple generators are often electrically 'noisy' and prone to produce spikes of quite high voltage that can damage sensitive electronic instruments. Thus, care should be taken, in respect of any equipment it is planned to 'plug-in'. A typical outboard magneto wiring diagram is shown in Illustration 82, Fig B.

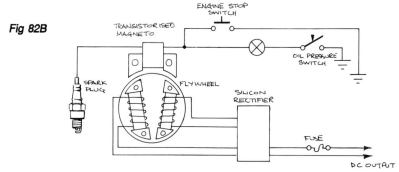

Fig 82B

Note that the engine 'stop' facility shorts out the magneto coil, so no voltage is generated, as the magnetic field tries to die away.

In a Capacitor Discharge (CD) System (Illustration 83), as the name suggests, a Capacitor is first charged and then, at the correct moment, discharged into an ignition coil. This generates the very high voltage required to activate the sparking plug. The Capacitor has to be charged to a voltage of about 200V DC. To achieve this it is necessary to either: generate a large AC voltage from a coil, placed close to a flywheel magnet (as in the magneto system); or to have a transistor oscillator circuit producing an AC output that can be transformed into a large AC voltage by a step-up transformer. Whichever method is employed, it is necessary to rectify the AC voltage into DC, so that it can charge the Capacitor. Once charged it is necessary to discharge the Capacitor, at just the right time, to correctly 'fire' the spark plug. This is done by sensing the engine timing with contact breaker points, or some other form of inductive, or optical sensor, as previously detailed in the section concerning inboard petrol engines. When the correct time for discharge is sensed, an electronic switch, usually a silicon controlled rectifier (SCR), is turned on and the Capacitor allowed to discharge into the primary winding of an ignition coil. This, in turn, causes a large voltage to be produced at the coil's secondary winding, which ignites the sparking plug.

The Capacitor Discharge System

Illustration Eighty Three   A Capacitor Discharge System Circuit

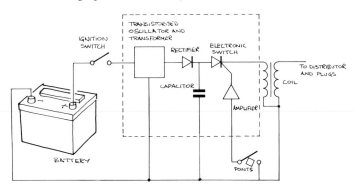

Some capacitor discharge systems use Surface Gap Sparking Plugs (Illustration 84). This type of plug, coupled with the very short but high voltage spark that CD systems produce, results in reduced fouling and increased reliability.

Surface Gap Sparking Plug

Illustration Eighty Four   A Surface Gap Sparking Plug

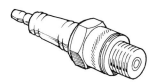

A development of the Outboard Motor becoming increasingly popular, probably because of its 'green appeal', is the electric (or battery) powered unit. They are 'eerily' quiet, economical, reliable and pollution free, and are favoured in the USA, where legislation has made them mandatory on some of the Great Lakes.

Electric Outboard Motors

Various models are available and performance is usually measured in 'lbs of thrust'. The larger units can develop up to 50lbs of thrust, and are capable of powering a boat weighing in excess of 2500lbs. Power consumption is obviously a major factor in their usefulness and an average sized motor gives three to four hours 'motoring', from a 75 Ah capacity battery.

Their deployment is limited to inland waters, and it will be interesting to see if they catch on in the UK.

A few Inboard mounted, electric powered narrow boats have been developed for use on the canals. They can run for up to six hours, between rechargings. This innovation is gradually becoming more viable as battery technology advances, but it is unlikely that they will sell in large numbers, in the foreseeable future..., or will they?

Electric Inboard Motors

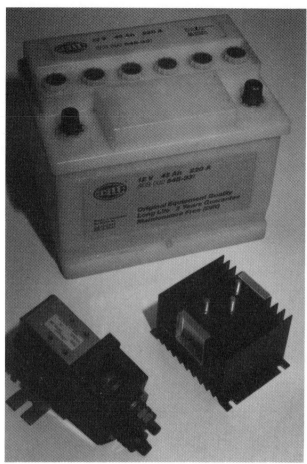

CHAPTER SEVEN

DISTRIBUTING THE POWER

All the generation and power unit equipment, usually found in and around the engine room were detailed, in Chapters 5 and 6.

Beyond the Engine Room

Most craft are equipped to 'support' other electric driven 'gizmos', in order to facilitate human needs, even if only for occasional weekends. These include such items as lights, pumps, and other miscellanea. This Chapter deals with getting the power to them, from the battery. A simple method would be to lead individual pairs of wire to each piece of electrical equipment, directly from the battery. Work it will, but... apart from much wasted wire, not to mention the inordinate number of hours necessary to install it all, there would be far too many cables, emanating from the environs of the battery and the engine room. The whole arrangement would resemble nothing more than a wiring nightmare of a railway marshalling yard.

Not surprisingly, a simpler and preferred method is to utilise a Distribution Panel, also known as a Switch or Fuse Panel. These provide an elegant and practical method of distributing electrical power throughout the craft. A Distribution Panel is simply a board through which are mounted a number of switches and fuses, or circuit breakers. The front of the Panel is usually signed with labels that describe what each switch/ fuse/circuit breaker controls and or protects. The reverse side of the panel (hopefully) 'displays' neatly arranged cables and wires routed to and from the fuses, switches or circuit breakers, to deliver power to the various electrical equipment and fittings.

The Distribution Panel

Panel Siting

Illustration 85, Fig A outlines a typical Distribution Switch/Fuse) Panel layout. In a small sailing boat, it is usually mounted in or around the area used as a chart table (Illustration 85, Fig B), whilst in a power boat a popular position is the reverse side of the main cockpit/cabin bulkhead (Illustration 85, Fig C), whilst inland waterways craft usually have one positioned just inside the aft cockpit doors (Illustration 85, Fig D).

Illustration Eighty Five   Typical Distribution (or Switch/Fuse) Panels

Typical Panel Layout

Fig 85A

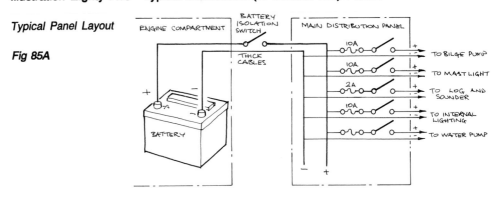

Siting for a Sailing Craft

...for a Power Boat

...for an Inland Waterways Craft

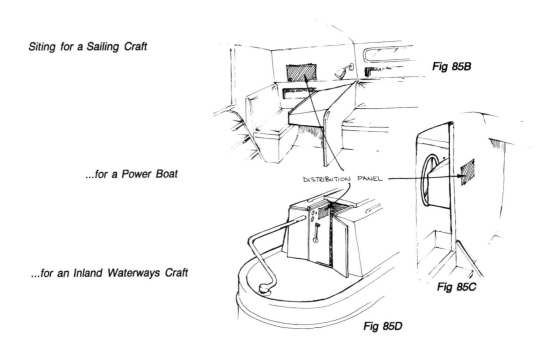

Fig 85B

Fig 85C

Fig 85D

Considerations in positioning a Distribution Panel include mounting it:-
(a) as close to the battery/batteries as is possible
(b) in an unexposed spot
(c) at a level which allows easy sight of the switch positions and fuses.

Most modern panels incorporate a fuse and switch for each circuit to which it distributes power (Illustration 86).

Illustration Eighty Six   Panel Fuses & Switches

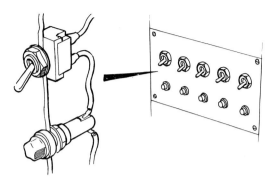

The benefits of a well-engineered distribution panel are that it:-
(a) Reduces the amount of wiring by only requiring a single pair of thick cables from the battery to the panel, and then short lengths of thinner, thus less expensive, wire to the individual electrical items. This arrangement not only reduces the amount of wiring required, but results in fewer unwanted voltage drops throughout the system.
(b) Allows individual electrical circuits, such as all the navigation lights, to be fused and switched on and off easily, from one position.
(c) Provides a convenient place from which to wire additional equipment, that may be added at a later date.

Fuses

Fuses are basically lengths of wire that have a known, maximum power rating. They have a certain value of resistance, usually very small (less than an ohm), although some low current fuses can have a resistance of 10 ohms, or more.

Fuses are designed to work using the knowledge that, when current flows, a small voltage is dropped, and hence power is dissipated, in the form of heat. When the current, through a fuse, reaches the maximum rating, the power dissipated is large enough to burn, and thus 'waste' the fuse wire. Removing the link stops all the current flowing through the circuit being protected.

Fuses, when placed in series with an electrical wire, are, in effect, a weak link in the circuit. They are deployed to protect the wiring and switches of a particular circuit, not to safeguard an item of equipment. Where the latter protection is required, the equipment will be separately fused. The current rating of a fuse must always be less than the maximum current rating of the wire and switches. This ensures that, in the event of something going wrong, and excessive current being taken by the circuit, the fuse will 'blow', prior to any other items being exposed to the danger (Illustration 87).

Illustration Eighty Seven   A Fuse in Circuit

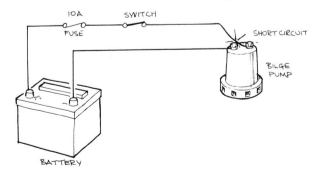

In this example a bilge pump has been bumping around in the depths of the hull. Unfortunately the positive connector has worked loose, dropped off, and become wedged between the two terminals of the bilge pump. This state of affairs provides an 'excellent' short circuit between the positive and negative terminals.

If the switch is closed (or turned on) a considerable amount of current will attempt to flow through the circuit (much larger than 10A). As soon as the current equals, or becomes greater than 10A, the fuse will blow and stop the current flowing.

If the circuit had not been fused, the only limiting factors on the amount of current flowing would be:-

(a) The battery capacity. Most batteries can easily provide 100A, for at least a few minutes, which is enough current to do quite a lot of damage to most installations.

(b) The cable used to wire in the pump. All wires have a maximum current rating, which varies with the cross-sectional area and type of insulation. In this example the cable used would probably have a cross-sectional area of between 2.5mm² and 4mm², which could cope with a maximum of some 20A (For details in respect of wires and cable ratings See Illustration 89). If the battery produced 100A of current flow, then the wire would soon melt, burn and possibly cause a fire!

Circuit Breakers

An alternative to fuses are Circuit Breakers, which resemble a switch and can be turned on and off (Illustration 88).

Illustration Eighty Eight   Circuit Breakers

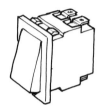

Like a fuse, a circuit breaker has a known resistance. The latter dissipates power, as the current flows, in the form of heat, which is utilised to cause a small bi-metallic strip (inside the circuit breaker) to bend. As the current reaches the maximum rating of the circuit breaker, the bi-metallic strip bends so much that it forces the circuit breaker's contacts apart, and stops the current flowing.

Circuit Breakers vis-a-vis Fuses

The benefit of circuit breakers, vis-a-vis fuses, are that they are:-

(a) Resettable, whereas fuses have to be replaced, requiring a selection of different spares to be stowed. Circuit breakers can be fitted, and forgotten.

(b) Both a fuse and switch, in one unit, cutting down on wiring and connections behind the distribution panel.

There has to be a downside, doesn't there? In this case it is that Circuit Breakers are, as yet, more expensive than a separate fuse and switch arrangement. (They would be, wouldn't they!).

In previous chapters, it has been mentioned that wires have a small amount of resistance. Furthermore it has been stated that where large currents are flowing in long lengths of wire, unwanted volt drops result. It has also been 'touched upon' that wires have a maximum current rating.

As the resistance and maximum current rating are both effected by the thickness, or cross-sectional area, of the wire, it is important to be aware of typical values, for different types of wire. This knowledge enables a user to calculate the best size of wire, for any particular application.

Wire Ratings

The Table (Illustration 89, Fig A), which follows, gives a fairly good idea of maximum current ratings and resistance values for most common sizes of multi-strand, flexible wire. Incidentally, the use of solid, single core wire is not recommended on boats - it is much more prone to suffer metal fatigue and breakage, when subjected to movement or vibration, over long periods of time.

Wire is usually identified by the number of strands that make up the conductor and the diameter of each strand. For instance, a reel of wire labelled "24/0.20" has a conductor consisting of 24 strands of 0.2mm diameter copper wire.

Illustration Eighty Nine   Wire Rating Table & Terms

Fig 89A

Cross Sectional Area (C.S.A.)	Conductors	Strand Wire Gauge (S.W.G.)	Wall Thickness	Outside Diameter (O.D.)	Max Current	DC Voltage* Drop
0.05mm²	16/0.2mm	22	0.08mm	2.6mm	3A	83.00mV
0.75mm²	24/0.2mm	20	0.08mm	2.9mm	6A	56.00mV
1.00mm²	32/0.2mm	18	0.08mm	3.1mm	10A	43.00mV
1.05mm²	30/0.25mm	16	0.08mm	3.4mm	15A	31.00mV
2.05mm²	50/0.25mm	14	0.08mm	3.8mm	20A	18.00mV
4.00mm²	56/0.3mm	12	0.08mm	4.4mm	25A	11.00mV
6.00mm²	84/0.3mm	10	0.08mm	5.1mm	44A	7.09mV
10.00mm²	80/0.4mm	8	1.02mm	6.8mm	60A	4.06mV
16.00mm²	126/0.4mm	6	1.58mm	9.2mm	81A	2.09mV
25.00mm²	196/0.4mm	4	1.58mm	10.6mm	105A	1.09mV

* Voltage drop per amp per metre.

If a wire is not clearly marked, then the best method of ascertaining its type is to measure the outside diameter (OD).

The usual insulation for electric wires and cables is made from PVC (*polyvinyl chloride*) which is more than acceptable, for most applications. However, where cables might encounter high temperatures, acid, oil, or long exposure to ultra violet light (i.e. the sun), then PTFE (*Poly Tetra Fluoro Ethylene*) insulated wires are ideal, though expensive. A compromise, to deal with the above conditions, would be to use silicone rubber insulated wire, which is cheaper than PTFE. One other insulation that may be encountered is Butyl, commonly used for battery cables.

Illustration 89, Fig B, indicates some of the terms used when describing wires. The conductors are normally bare copper. It is possible to purchase tinned copper wire, which is ideal where solder is to be used, and should last longer in a marine environment.

Fig 89B

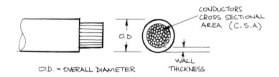

OD is short for overall or outside diameter; the wall thickness is the thickness of the insulation; the CSA is the cross-sectional area of the conductor; and all measurements are in millimetres. SWG indicates Standard Wire Gauge, and is another method of describing a wire's size (See Chapter 12).

The (previous) Table lists a figure for voltage drop, in millivolts*, for a particular wire. To expand, that is the amount of voltage a wire will drop, or 'shed', for every ampere of current flowing, along each and every metre of the wire. This may appear rather confusing, but is very easy to use, in practice.

*1 millivolt (1mV) = 1/1000V

The following examples illustrate how to use the Table:-

Example 1:

The owner of a motorboat wishes to mount a 12V, 80W spotlight on the bow of his boat. The distribution panel is in the passageway, towards the stern of the craft. After routing the wire through and around various bulkheads and internal linings, it is determined that two pieces of wire, each 5m long, will be required.

To calculate the current required by the spotlight, use our 'old friend', the formula:-

Power (watts) = Voltage (V) x Current (A)

or

Current = Power ÷ Voltage

Therefore the Current = 80W ÷ 12V

Thus the Current = 6.75A.

The current must flow from the battery to the light, and then all the way back again, thus the total distance travelled is:- 10m (2 x 5m)

Empirical Formula for Voltage Drop

At this point it is opportune to advise of the empirical rule, for Voltage Drops, which is never to design a circuit with a Volt Drop larger than 5% of a battery's voltage. This approximately equates to 0.5V, for a 12V system, and 1.0V, for a 24V system.

With this in mind, divide the maximum allowable volt drop for a 12V system (which is 0.5V) by the current flowing multiplied by the distance it has to travel - which gives a figure for the volt drop per metre per ampere. Thus:-

Volt drop = 0.5V ÷ (6.75A x 10m)

= 7.4mV (or 0.0074V).

Using the Table (Illustration 89, Fig A), it is possible to read off which wire will best suit these needs. The thinnest wire that has a volt drop figure of 7.4mV, or less, is the 84/0.3mm wire. (The only reasons to use the thinnest wire, that meets the volt drop requirement, is that the thicker the wire, the more expensive, the less flexible, and thus less easy it is to install).

It is worth noting that even though current required for the spotlight is 6.75A, which could easily be accommodated by the conductor 32/0.2mm (max current 10A), this wire would not be suitable. This is because the voltage drop would equal (in volt drop per metre per ampere), reading off the required values from the same table:-

Volt drop x current (or amperage) x distance

Therefore, 43mV x 6.75A x 10m = 0.675V.

This is in excess of the empirical value allowed of 0.5V.

Example 2

A boat owner wishes to add an extra 15W light, to the two 15W lights already fitted in the main cabin. The existing lights are wired in parallel, using 24/0.2mm wire, with a voltage drop of 56mV, as sketched in Illustration 90, Fig A.

Illustration Ninety   Installation Calculations

Fig 90A

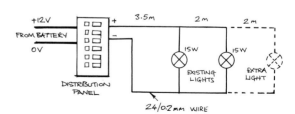

To calculate the extra current needed by the new light, and whether the existing wiring is adequate to cope, without creating too much of a volt drop, it is necessary to first calculate the current taken by a 15W light. As the lights are wired in parallel, each light has +12V across it and will dissipate the same power. As Power (watts) is calculated by multiplying Voltage (V) by Current (A), then the amperage equals watts divided by Volts:-

15 watts ÷ 12V = 1.25A

As there are to be three lights, and they each take the same current, then the total current demand is:-

1.25A x 3 = 3.75A

From the Table (Illustration 89, Fig A), it will be observed that the maximum current rating for 24/0.2mm wire is 6A, so the extra loading is well within its specification.

Illustration 90, Fig B sketches what happens, in Example 2, to the total current, as it flows into each of the three lights.

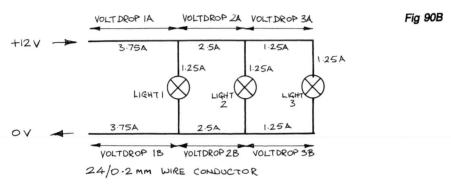

At first the current is at 3.75A, but then splits and decreases as 1.25A flows into the first bulb. This example also shows the separate volt drops in the circuit. Volt drops '1A' and '1B' are equal to each other and are the result of 3.75A of current flowing through 7m of wire (3½m from the distribution panel to Light 1 and 3½m back. Volt drops '2A' and '2B' are also equal, but will both be less than volt drops 1A and 1B, as they are the result of only 2.5A of current flowing through 4m of cable, from Light 1 to Light 2 and back. Finally, volt drops '3A' and '3B' are equal, the result of 1.25A flowing through 4m of wire. The total volt drop in the whole circuit equals the sum of the volt drops in 1A + 1B, plus 2A + 2B, plus 3A + 3B, which should be less than 0.5V, the maximum empirically allowed in a +12V system. Measuring volt drop (in volt drop per metre per amperes), and referring again to the Table (Illustration 89, Fig A) in respect of the wire rated 24/0.2mm, then:-

Volt drop 1A = 1B = 56mV x 3.50m x 3.75A
Volt drop 2A = 2B = 56mV x 2.00m x 2.50A
Volt drop 3A = 3B = 56mV x 2.00m x 1.25A

Therefore the Total of all the volt drops in this circuit (1A + 1B + 2A + 2B + 3A + 3B)

= 0.735V + 0.735V + 0.28V + 0.28V + 0.14V + 0.14V
= 2.31V.

This is 5 times more than the allowable empirical figure. Thus the existing wire will have to be replaced, with a thicker one, with a volt drop of approximately 1/5 of that of the existing 24/0.2mm wire, or some 11mV. Once more referring to the Table (Illustration 89, Fig A), it will be observed that 56/0.3mm wire is about the thinnest wire that can be used.

The quality of boat wiring is not always as good as it should be, and it is possible that up to 80% of electrical faults can be directly attributed to ineffective or poor wiring. With a small amount of knowledge, and a bit of common sense, most wiring related faults can be avoided.

Electrical Wiring

The Two-Wire Insulated Return

The most desirable method of marine wiring is the Two-Wire Insulated Return System. Despite the rather wordy title it is a quite straightforward arrangement. Simply put, it means that all the electrical items have the power supplied by two insulated wires. At first, this may seem a rather silly stipulation, as, surely, to make any equipment work it must have a positive and negative connection? On the other hand, consider the family car in which all the metalwork is earthed to the negative terminal of the battery, so only a positive wire needs to be routed to each item of equipment. Consequently, it might be thought that on a metal boat, and only a metal boat, the same method could be employed. But if it were, the more demanding marine environmental conditions would result in an electrolytic action, causing the metalwork to be literally eaten away, in a matter of months.

Incidentally, the latter phenomenon, and how to guard against it, is covered in more detail at the end of this Chapter. Despite the aforementioned, an instance where it is difficult to totally insulate the positive and negative supply involves the engine, and its ancillary electrics. This is because most electrical equipment associated with the engine, such as the starter motor, alternator, as well as the engine monitoring sensors, use the engine block, connected to the -ve battery terminal, to provide the negative supply. It is possible, as well as highly desirable, to absolutely isolate the engine from the -ve battery supply, but it may involve quite a lot of work and expense.

Stars & Chains

Wiring should, where possible, always start from a common point, be it the battery or a distribution panel, and finish at the first piece of equipment to which it is connected.

Illustration 91, Fig A sketches a Star wiring layout, with the battery in the centre.

Stars

Illustration Ninety One   'Star' & Chain Wiring Layouts

Fig 91A   A Star Installation

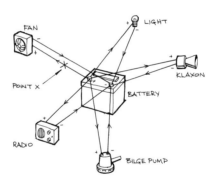

Chains

Illustration Ninety One, Fig B outlines a Chain wiring system.

Fig 91B   A Chain Installation

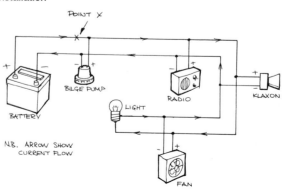

By comparing one with the other, a number of differences can be observed:-

(a) In the Star installation the current flowing to, say, the fan originates directly from the +ve battery terminal, passing through the fan and then returning directly to the -ve battery terminal.

(b) In the Chain installation the current to the fan must flow from the +ve battery terminal, past the bilge pump, radio and klaxon, at each of which a part of the current splits off, after which some of the remaining current flows through the fan, the rest going to the light. After flowing through the fan, the current rejoins all the other equipment current returns, as they flow back to the -ve battery terminal.

(c) In the Star system, if the fan is electrically 'noisy', that is to say it develops lots of little, high frequency voltage spikes on the positive and negative supply wires, then this is likely to be absorbed, or at least decreased, by the battery - the latter being an excellent 'absorbent' of electrical noise.

(d) In the Chain system, if the same fan developed electrical noise, then that would 'travel' past the klaxon, the radio and the bilge pump, prior to being absorbed by the battery. The effect of the noise 'passing' by the klaxon and the bilge pump would not be noticeable in their operation. On the other hand, a radio is very susceptible to electrical noise, which would probably be heard as a background hum or crackling.

(e) In the Star system only the fan would stop working, if a break in the wire were to occur at point X, whilst a similar fault at point X in the Chain system would 'knock out' all the equipment.

(f) In the Star System, each item is wired individually, thus requiring great lengths of conductor, in comparison to the Chain System, where, by using a little thought, the amount of wire needed can be kept to a minimum (Illustration 92, Figs A & B).

It has to be borne in mind that the wiring for a Chain Installation has to be thicker, in order to cope with the total current required by all the equipment.

Illustration Ninety Two   Star & Chain Wiring Requirements

Fig 92A   Star installation requiring approximately 40m of wire.

Fig 92B   A similar Chain installation only requires some 25m of wire.

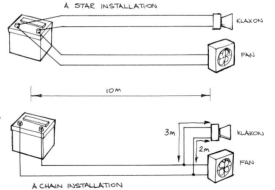

To summarise, a Star installation, vis-a-vis the Chain System, is less prone to electrical noise, and less likely to suffer from multiple equipment failure, but does require the purchase and installation of more wire.

Wherever possible, always wire the following in the Star manner: electrically noisy items, such as fans, motors, pumps and fluorescent lighting; navigation lights, as well as any other items where a failure could put safety at risk.

In fact, generally the only items to be wired in the Chain manner are internal lighting and, possibly, internal power sockets. Even then it is best to split the lighting into two chains, so that any fault would not result in a total blackout (Illustration 93).

Stars vis-a-vis Chain Installations

Illustration Ninety Three   More Chain Wiring

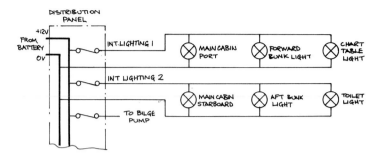

**Wiring
Connections**

Whatever type of wire or method of wiring is used, one thing is for certain - that they will require some sort of connector or connection, at both ends. The practicalities of connecting wires (crimping and soldering) have been covered in Chapter 1, but little mention was made about which connectors/connections are easily available and commonly used for particular marine applications.

*Crimp
Connectors*

By far the most popular, easiest method of connecting wires together, or to electrical equipment, is to use Crimps (Illustration 94).

Illustration Ninety Four   Crimp Connectors

Fig 94A   Flat plug & socket

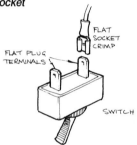

The most common form of Crimp Connectors. They tend to be used for connecting wires to switches, relays and other electrical equipment. The wire is fitted with the flat socket crimp connector and the equipment normally has a number of projecting plug terminals, to which the requisite socket can be connected.

Fig 94B   Flat plug/Blade Terminal

Sometimes referred to as a Blade Terminal. The standard width of the Plug is 6mm (¼"), although they are also available in 5mm (3/16") and 3mm (0.11") versions - so it is worth having a selection in the 'come-in-handy' box. Incidentally, Lucas's trade name for the 6mm flat plug connectors is Lucar Terminals.

Other less popular types of crimps, used in some applications, include the:-

Fig 94C   Flat Socket with Branch

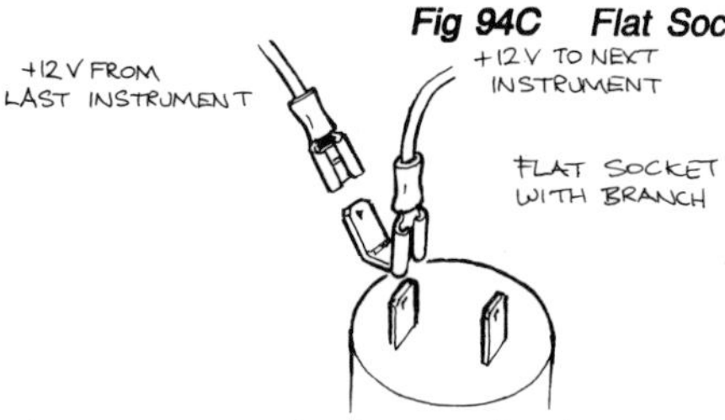

These are used for wiring into engine instruments and allow a wire to connect to a flat plug terminal, whilst providing another flat plug connection at the back of the crimp, for a second connection - great for looping the +12V and 0V supplies from instrument to instrument.

Fig 94D   Wire Pin

This type of crimp provides a neater method of fitting a wire to a screw terminal connector (chocolate block). The first sketch illustrates two wires, both fitted with wire pin crimps, to be joined using a screw terminal block.

The second sketch shows why Wire Pins are preferable, and the weakness of using 'untreated' multi-strand wire. As the screw is tightened down on the wire, it is possible for the strands to splay out and up the side of the hole, resulting in only a few strands of wire actually being secured. This will reduce the conductors cross-sectional area, and limit the wire's current carrying capacity. Not a good idea!

Fig 94E   Eyelets (crimps)

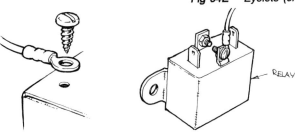

They allow wires to be connected to any item that has nut and bolts, or self-tapping screws, as fixings. The first sketch shows an eyelet being connected to the metal case of a piece of equipment, using a self-tapping screw - a common method of earthing the metal case of equipment that has a mains supply.

The second sketch illustrates a relay that has two nut and bolt connections, as well as two flat plug connections. (The relay switches when a voltage is applied between the two flat plug connections). Nut & bolt connections are designed to carry a larger current than flat plugs (and are usually used in applications where currents of 20A or more are likely to be flowing), and eyelets are the best type of crimp to use with them.

Fig 94F   Open Eyelets

Similar to closed eyelet crimps, but they should not be used in the same sort of way, unless absolutely necessary. Their disadvantage is that they can work loose and become disconnected, whereas closed eyelet crimps will only fall off when the bolt, or screw, is entirely removed. They might be considered applicable where the crimp fastening is to be connected, and disconnected, regularly, as the fixing will not have to be completely undone to allow disconnection.

Fig 94G Male & Female Bullet crimps

 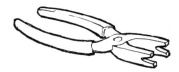

Probably make the best wire-to-wire connections, and are ideal for semi-permanent joins, that will only be disconnected occasionally. However, they fit together quite tightly, so strong fingers and a good grip are required to pull them apart. In fact, they are sometimes quite difficult to push together, thus a special tool exists, as shown. This type of crimp is rarely, if ever, found on new equipment fitted by the manufacturer.

There are two other types of Crimp connectors, but both are employed rather differently than the aforementioned connectors. They are the:-

Fig 94H Butt Connectors

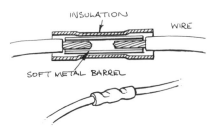

Provide a permanent method of connecting two wires together. They must not be used for fastening more than two wires, despite the temptation It is not the use for which the connector was designed, as they do not result in a satisfactory or strong enough joint.

Fig 94 I The Splice Connector,

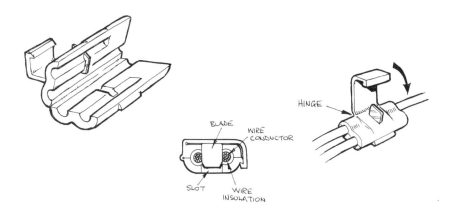

Also known as a Snap Lock and Scotch Lock. They are very useful for connecting a new wire to an old one, where the 'act' cannot be unified at a convenient terminal. The device consists of a hinged plastic body that houses a slotted metal blade. Note that neither the existing or new wire need be cut and stripped back, unlike all the other crimp connectors previously described.

Once the wires are in position, the blade must be squeezed into the splice, until it is flush with the body, using a pair of general purpose pliers. As the blade is pushed into the body, it cuts through or displaces the insulation of the wires, making contact with both the conductors, thus making a connection between them. Once in position, the plastic clip is bent into place, so that it holds the hinged body together. Despite, perhaps, appearing a rather poor method of 'joining', if used correctly, these connectors are very reliable. They are popular in the automobile industry, for the installation of additional electric supplies, such as towing lighting sets, and in other situations where optional (electrical) extras have to be fitted.

Terminal Blocks, sometimes referred to as 'chocolate' blocks, are another handy method of connecting wires (Illustration 95). They are usually purchased in strips of 12 blocks, each of which is isolated from the others and can be used to connect 2 or more wires together. Strips can easily be cut up with a Stanley knife, hacksaw or side cutters. Terminal Blocks are often used where lots of wires need to be connected together, such as in the distribution or engine instrument panel. They also have the facility to be easily fastened to a convenient fixing, with screws.

Terminal Blocks

Illustration Ninety Five   Terminal Blocks

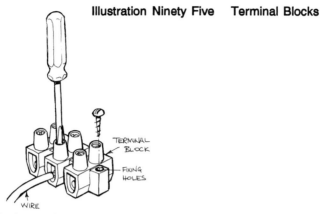

Another type of Terminal Block is the earth-connecting strip. These are not insulated from each other as they are used for linking all the 0V connections together. They are normally made from zinc-plated brass, and are commonly available in blocks of 4 or 8, which respectively allows the connection of 8 or 16 wires.

It is often desirable to have a handy means of connecting and disconnecting equipment from its supply, where the equipment is only occasionally used, or is of a high value. The fitting of Plugs and Sockets allows easy removal, when required (Illustration 96).

Plugs & Sockets

Illustration Ninety Six   Plugs & Sockets

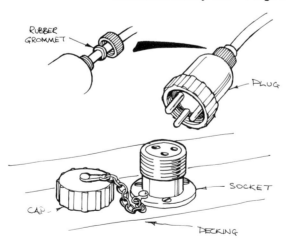

Wiring Plugs to the wire tail of a piece of equipment, and having a series of Sockets around a craft, allows quick connection and disconnection. A host of different Plugs and Sockets are available, ranging from low-cost, internal-use only types, to more expensive, fully waterproof, 'even when fully immersed' fittings. For most applications 2 pin Plugs and Sockets are all that is required to provide a +ve and -ve supply to any item. With more and more electronic equipment being fitted, it is not unusual for 3, 4, 5 or more pin Plugs and Sockets to be required, for wind transducers, autopilots, instrument systems, and radio sets.

Probably the best Plugs and Sockets for power connections are the newer style, glass-filled, nylon or polycarbonate fittings that are waterproof and dustproof (to IP66 B.S.5490). They are primarily designed for external use, but if the extra money can be found, it is worthwhile fitting them throughout.

When assembling Plugs and Sockets, smear the wire connections with silicone grease, even filling the inner body. Where mounting the Socket to a bulkhead, use a silicone rubber or other sealant for the mating faces of the Socket and bulkhead. If fitting thru' deck, external connectors remember that they are only as good as the installation and maintenance they receive. Corrosion will result in poor, or non-existent connections, and may 'ensure' more trouble than they are worth. For this reason, check and grease Plugs and Sockets, at least once a season, and always fit the accompanying protective screw-on caps, when they are disconnected.

Switches

Switches are the 'water taps' of the electrical world and control the power, by stopping and starting the 'flow' through the system. Despite the wide variety available, marine Switches can generally be 'broken down' into five types (Illustration 97, Fig A).

Illustration Ninety Seven   Switch Types

Fig 97A Electrical Characteristics

(1) *Push Button: Used for applications where items only need to be switched on for short periods, such as a klaxon.*

(2) *Single Pole Single Throw (SPST): The most popular and cheapest type of switch, used as a general purpose, on/off switch.*

(3) *Single Pole Double Throw (SPDT): Used where a 2 function selector is required, such as auto/manual bilge pump switch.*

(4) *Double Pole Single Throw (DPST): Popular for applications where both the positive and negative connections have to be switched off, such as a battery isolation switch.*

(5) *Double Throw Double Throw (DPDT): Used for 2 function selector switch applications, where both the positive and negative connections have to be switched, such as a battery changeover/selector switch.*

Most Switches are toggle or rocker operated (Illustration 97, Fig B). Electrically there is usually little or no difference between them, thus the choice rests between whichever looks best, in a particular position. Rocker switches are rather more difficult to install, as they require a square cut-out, whereas toggle units simply need a round, hole to accommodate the threaded body of the switch.

Fig 97B Toggle or Rocker Switches.

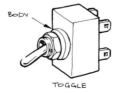

TOGGLE

ROCKER

The standard connector for marine Switches is the 6mm (¼") flat plug (*See* Illustration 94, Fig A). Owners requiring to stock some spare Switches should consider purchasing DPDT units, as they can be employed in place of all the other types, by only using some of the connections.

All Switches have a maximum current rating (which is normally quoted for 250V AC and 28V DC), and a maximum 'on' resistance. This latter resistance is usually 0.1 ohms, or less, though this tends to increase with age, as the switch contacts become worn and or dirty. The reason for the desirability of the very low resistance (remembering Ohms Law, where Voltage (V) = Current (A) x Resistance (ohms), or Ohms = V ÷ A) is that it is the combination of current and voltage that causes Switches to heat up, and incur damage. Keeping the resistance to a minimum, ensures the current portion of the equation is subject of a small multiplier.

It is possible to purchase marine Switches with a maximum current rating of up to 20A. If it is required to switch greater currents, then it will be necessary to 'wire in' a relay.

Relays are electrically actuated switches (Illustration 98, Fig A).

Relays

Illustration Ninety Eight   Relays

Fig 98A External Connections

Instead of being mechanically operated, by pushing a button or moving a lever, Relays are activated by applying voltage at two of their connections. Inside the unit is a coil of wire, the actuator, and two contacts - one fixed, the other made from 'springy' metal, so that it can move. When a voltage is applied to the coil, current flows through it and sets up a magnetic field (around the coil). This field attracts the moveable contact which swings towards the coil, making impact with the fixed contact, thus the switching action occurs, and current can flow through the Relay (Illustration 98, Fig B). The two contacts remain touching, until the voltage is removed from the coil, at which point the moveable contact springs back - switching off the Relay (Illustration 98, Fig B).

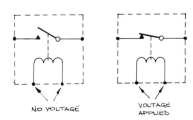

Fig 98B Internal Operation

Illustration 98, Fig C sketches differently operated Relays.

Fig 98C Different Types of Relay Operating 'Internals'

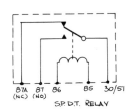

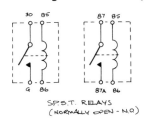

Relays have a maximum current rating, similar to switches, but generally much higher (50A or more). It is recommended that Relays (and switches) have a safety factor of a third (some 133 1/3%), if only to ensure a 'good' life.

As an example, where it is required to switch 18A of current, a 20A switch is not the answer (as 20A represents only about a 112.5% ratio). Instead, a 30A Relay should be fitted, which will switch the required current safely, for a longer period.

Relays can be easily checked using a meter. Set the meter to measure resistance, remove all connections to the particular fitting, and then check the reading of the resistance across the two coil terminals. The latter can usually be identified by numbers marked on the relay - 85 and 86 are those popularly used by European manufacturers to label the coil terminals (Illustration 99).

Illustration Ninety Nine   Relay Markings & Testing

Fig 99A   Lucas Relay Marking

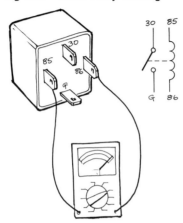

Fig 99B   European Relay Marking

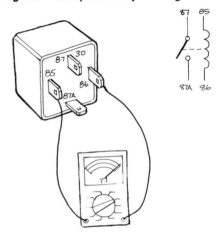

The usual relay resistance, measured across the coil terminals, is between 50 ohms and 100 ohms. Once the coil has been monitored, the switch contact resistance should be checked. To do this, refix the two wires, previously connected to the coil (plug) terminals, and turn on (or energise) the Relay, by operating the switch that normally activates the piece of equipment connected to the Relay. Measure the resistance across the other two (plug) terminals, for which the reading should be less than 0.1 ohms.

Wiring Practicalities

It is all very well to airily refer to '...wiring in a light here, a pump over there and a radio by the chart table'. But how is it done, without loops of unsightly wires scattered about, all over the place? Wiring a boat 'from scratch', is a comparatively easy job, in terms of tucking the cables away out of sight. Inner linings and fashion pieces can hide a lot of defects... and cover various wires. However, when adding a new piece of equipment to a craft, it may well be necessary to remove panels and linings, in order to route the wire in such a way as to not look tatty and amateurish. If this is too difficult, then at least tuck them away out of sight, beneath the side deck, under a convenient stringer, or in the angle of adjacent bulkheads. A last resort is to utilise the underside of any cabin carpet, but preferably beneath a piece that is not walked on regularly!

An alternative is to fit plastic conduit, or trunking, which protect and give an aesthetic, pleasing finish to a job.

Conduit

Conduit (Illustration 100, Fig A) is available in various diameters, from 10mm to 25mm, is very flexible, will withstand a certain amount of physical abuse (and thus is very useful for protecting wiring in and around the engine room), is comparatively inexpensive, and is easy to fit.

Illustration One Hundred   Wiring Practicalities

Fig 100A Conduit

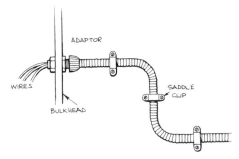

It can easily be bent into most positions or shapes, can easily be cut to whatever length is required, with a sharp knife, and can be secured to a cabin wall or bulkhead, using saddle clips and self-tapping screws, or nylon cable ties. Wherever wires have to pass through a bulkhead, either drill and radius a hole big enough to take the wires and Conduit, or purchase an adaptor that can be attached to the bulkhead. The latter makes a neater, more professional termination to the Conduit. As a bonus, push-fit adaptors are available, that can be pressed into the ends of the Conduit, allowing one piece to be joined to another.

Trunking (Illustration 100, Fig B) is plastic, square or rectangular in section, and ranges in size from 16mm x 16mm to 38mm x 25mm. It is sold in cut lengths and two parts. The main body of the Trunking is secured by self-tapping screws, after which the wires are routed inside, and the job finished off with, a clip-on cover.

Trunking

Fig 100B Trunking

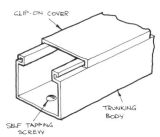

Like conduit, Trunking is easy to work and can be cut with a sharp knife or small hacksaw. Despite, probably, being more attractive to the eye, than conduit, Trunking is not flexible and cannot be bent to shape. A number of accessories are available for use with Trunking, including couplings for connecting two pieces together, 90° angle pieces, for changing direction, 'T' pieces for splitting the trunking off in two directions, and end pieces to neatly terminate the installation.

Cable clips or Ties are commonly available and allow wires to be gathered neatly together (Illustration 100, Fig C).

Cable Ties

Fig 100C Cable Ties

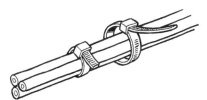

Not only do they make a wiring job look more professional, but they assist in ensuring 'the occasional' wire does not hang 'down and about', in danger of getting caught up in some whirling piece of machinery. Cable Ties are normally made of nylon and have a little, ratchet type catch. This allows the strap to be tightened, without coming undone. Ties are not only very quick and easy to use, but are far better than the old method of fastening cables together, which involved using waxed lacing cord, with lots of little knots, at regular intervals.

Grommets   Grommets should be used, wherever a wire has to pass through a metal or plastic panel or plate (Illustration 100, Fig D).

Fig 100D

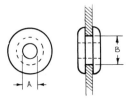

The Dimension 'A' should be slightly less than the outside diameter of the wire, to give a good 'splash-proof' connection.
   Dimension 'B' is the diameter of the hole to be cut through any panel, in order to accommodate the Grommet.

Cable Glands   Sharp edges can, after a period of time, wear through the insulation of cables and wires, thus damaging them, and possibly causing a short circuit, with the ever-present possibility of fire. Best to fit a grommet! Cable Glands are similar to grommets, but more substantial and offer a very good seal against water, even under pressure (Illustration 100, Fig E).

Fig 100E   Cable Glands

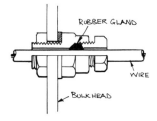

As the nut is tightened, the rubber gland is compressed and squeezes snugly around the cable, making an excellent weatherproof seal. A variation on the 'cable gland theme' is the waterproof deck gland, developed to facilitate the ability to pass wires through the deck of a craft, without incurring leaks.

Wiring Loops   When installing a piece of equipment it is important to allow plenty of wire at the connections, in order that the cables can have a 'stress free loop'. Wiring straight to a terminal block can not only place the wires under tension, but any vibration or strain would stress them. Conversely any vibration, or pulling movement, on a looped installation is absorbed (Illustration 101).

Illustration One Hundred & One   Wiring Loops

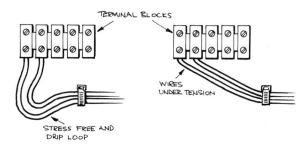

Another advantage of allowing for a Stress Loop is that the same doubles-up as a Drip Loop, which stops water creeping along wires, and contaminating the equipment.

Water Repelling Grease   All connections, that are likely to be subject to water contamination, should be covered in silicone grease, or *Vaseline*. Their application may make disconnecting the wires messy, but both compounds greatly increase the chances of connections lasting longer than one season, without suffering corrosion.

Some people recommend using a water repellent aerosol spray, but their properties can be short-lived, added to which they tend to attract dirt. Despite this, if neither silicone grease or *Vaseline* is available, then apply some!

A major problem experienced, when immersing boats in water, is Corrosion. Those who can remember their school chemistry lessons may recall that some metals corrode more easily than others. To save any back-up research, or memory delving, there follows a Table (llustration 102, Fig A), that lists the Nobility, or the electro-chemical series. At the top is magnesium, which is the metal that is the least resistant to Corrosion, whilst at the bottom is the metal gold, which does not corrode at all, under normal circumstances.

Galvanic Corrosion

Nobility

Illustration One Hundred & Two   The Nobility Table & 'Battery' Effect

Table of Nobility

Fig 102A *Electro-chemical Series, or Table of Nobility*

Least noble	Magnesium
	Magnesium alloy
	Zinc
	Galvanised iron
	Cadmium
	Aluminium
	Mild steel
	Cast iron
	Lead
	Tin
	Manganese bronze
	Brass
	Copper
	Stainless steel
	Nickel
	Silver
Most noble	Gold

Metals corrode because a chemical reaction takes place when two different metals are immersed, close to each other, in water. This occurs due to an electrical voltage being present between any two dissimilar metals. One of the metals will have more electrons than the other. These extra electrons will attempt to flow to the other piece of metal, through the water, which acts as a conductor - similar, really, to a battery cell. The most noble of any two metals has the least electrons, and is referred to as the cathode, whilst the least noble metal has the most electrons, and becomes the anode. Nature ensures that the extra electrons from the anode, flow through the water to the cathode, in the form of an electric current (Illustration 102, Fig B).

The 'Battery' Effect

Fig 102B *Nobility's 'Battery' Effect*

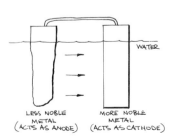
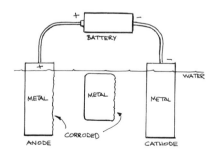

The corrosion is speeded up if either an external voltage is applied between the two pieces of metal, or if a current is flowing through one or both pieces of metal. This occurs because the voltage difference between the two metals is magnified and, hence, increases the current that flows between them. This state of affairs takes place, naturally, when any external metal part is connected, say, to the engine, which as has been explained is more often than not used as a common, negative earth for the engine electric circuits.

Unfortunately galvanic corrosion cannot be entirely stopped. The best that can be achieved is to increase the life of any metal hull or external metal hull fittings.

Minimising Galvanic Corrosion

There are three major aims to consider in Minimising Galvanic Corrosion.

(1) Materials - metals that are immersed, or in contact with water, including all skin-fittings, fastenings, rudders, propellers, if not the hull itself, should be carefully selected, to be as close to each other as possible on the Table of Nobility. The further apart any two metals are (in terms of Nobility), the quicker corrosion occurs.

Where possible all metal surfaces should be primed with anti-corrosion primer (not lead based), and if antifouling is to be directly applied, then it should not be copper or bronze based.

(2) Poor Electrical Installations - it is very important that all metals in permanent contact with water are at exactly the same voltage level. If they are not, the rate of corrosion will be increased. To ensure this, it is common practice to 'bond' the external metal objects to each other, with a thick copper braid, or copper strip, that has a very low resistance value. Once 'bonded' together, a single connection is made to the negative battery supply (Illustration 103).

Illustration One Hundred & Three   Bonding

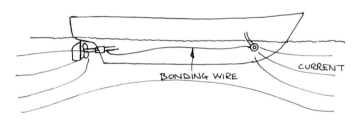
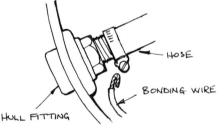

Where 'bonding' is installed correctly, galvanic corrosion is considerably minimised. If, however, through poor installation, or water ingress, a small leakage current from one of the positive battery supply circuits flows into the bonding circuit, then a voltage difference between the bonded items will occur, with unpleasant results.

Checking Current Leaks

To check for 'stray' currents in the hull, or hull fittings, carry out the following procedures:-

(a) Isolate the boat's battery, by turning off the battery isolator switch, or by disconnecting the +ve battery terminal.

(b) After turning on every piece of electrical equipment, use an electrical meter, set to the highest resistance range, to measure the resistance of the main positive supply to each of the hull fittings (and hull, if it is metal). If any of these are less than 100,000 ohms (100 k ohms), then there is a leak through which stray current can flow.

Unfortunately, to locate 'leaks' is a very tedious task which involves checking:-

(a) All the wiring, for poor joints and broken insulation.

(b) For water contamination of joints.

(c) That wiring or wires are not touching fittings, pipework or bulkheads.

Anything that looks suspect should be re-wired, cleaned, moved or relocated, and then the resistance checks repeated.

Sacrificial Anodes

(3) Sacrificial Anodes - once the various steps, already described, have been carried out, it is necessary to fit Sacrificial Anodes. As aforementioned, when two metals are submersed in water, the less noble metal loses its electrons to the more noble metal, and the less noble metal corrodes. To turn the tables on nature and take advantage of this fact, Sacrificial Anodes are fashioned from either of the least noble metals - zinc or magnesium. This ensures that they are always less noble than the metals

employed in the craft's construction, and that they corrode first, and not the hull or hull fittings.

Sacrificial Anodes are available in all shapes and sizes. The number and types to be fitted depend upon the size and material of a particular hull, and whether the craft is used in fresh or sea-water. For instance inland waterway, freshwater anodes are manufactured from magnesium, whilst sea-water anodes are zinc based. Sacrificial Anodes are usually hull mounted (Illustration 104, Fig A).

Illustration One Hundred & Four   Sacrificial Anodes

Fig 104A

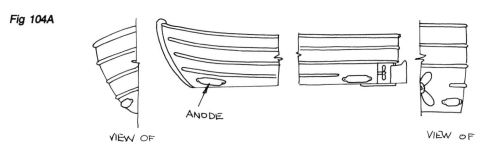

Generally, metal and GRP hulls only require protection for the thru' hull fittings, thus one or two anodes will suffice. This is in contrast to wooden hulls, where all the hull planking fastenings have to be taken into account.

Other types of anode are available for fitting to a boat's engine, rudder, skeg, keel, or propeller shaft (Illustration 104, Fig B).

Fig 104B

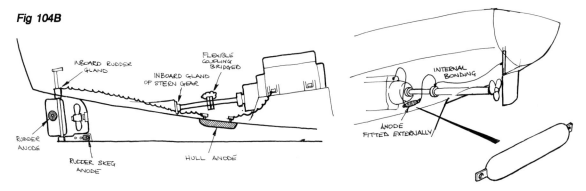

Anodes fitted to wood or GRP hulls are usually thru' bolted so that bonding cables can be connected to the bolts, inside the hull (Illustration 104, Fig C).

Fig 104C   *Fig 104D*

The anodes of a metal hull (or fittings) are often welded (Illustration 104, Fig D).

It must be stressed that owners and builders, as well as any other person, involved in fitting anodic protection, should consult the manufacturer's of this type of equipment, prior to 'activating' any particular course of action. They are only too willing to advise on the best course of action.

Illustration One Hundred & Five   Approved Navigation Light Layouts

Fig 105A

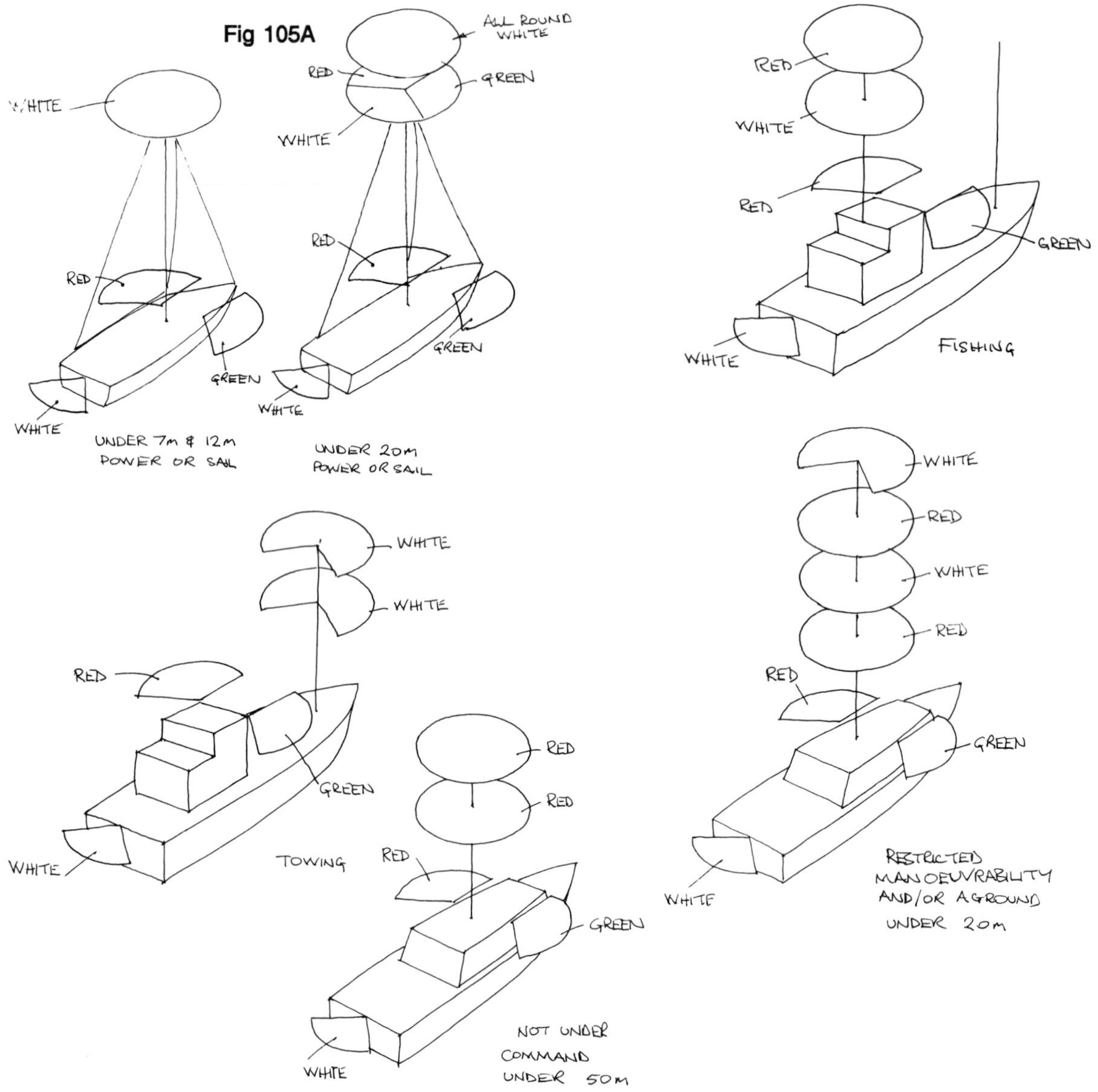

ALL ROUND WHITE

WHITE

RED   GREEN

WHITE

RED

RED

GREEN

WHITE

WHITE

UNDER 7m & 12m
POWER OR SAIL

UNDER 20m
POWER OR SAIL

RED

WHITE

RED

GREEN

WHITE

FISHING

WHITE

WHITE

RED

GREEN

WHITE

TOWING

RED

RED

RED

GREEN

WHITE

NOT UNDER
COMMAND
UNDER 50m

WHITE

RED

WHITE

RED

RED

GREEN

WHITE

RESTRICTED
MANOEUVRABILITY
AND/OR AGROUND
UNDER 20m

These sketches have been detailed, not simply to show the minimum requirements, but more the acceptable 'norm' for craft respectively under 7m, under 12m, and under 20m, in length. It is possible to refine the fittings down, depending on whether a boat is power or sail, and its actual size.

CHAPTER EIGHT

USING THE POWER

Lighting

Lighting is essential for owners of craft who intend to cruise after dark, and or overnight on board. In fact, navigation lights are a mandatory, as set out in the 'Merchant Shipping (Distress Signals and Prevention of Collisions) Regulations, 1983'. To be truly accurate, users of the inland waterway canal system are subject to the caveat that these regulations are to be followed, "...so far as is practicable. In particular, the range of visibility and height of the lights may be departed from because of the physical limitations of the navigation, but their number and character must be adhered to".

Generally, the lighting needs of most boats' lighting needs can be divided into external and internal. Despite both being necessary, they serve different purposes and require disparate knowledge to install and maintain.

External Lighting
Navigation Lights

The most ubiquitous external lighting must be the Navigation Lights. Anyone contemplating night cruising, even for short periods, as stated, must have approved Navigation Lights, fitted in accordance with the 'Survey of Lights and Signalling Equipment' regulations (Illustration 105, Fig A). It is worth bearing in mind that owners not following these rules are probably nullifying their insurance cover...! An outline of the basics ensues, but for up-to-date, detailed information, it is advisable to obtain a copy of them, as published by HMSO, from the Department of Trade.

Navigation Lights, commonly installed on leisure craft, are as follows:-

Sidelights

(a) Sidelights. They are fitted in pairs, the red light to the port (or left-hand) side, and the green light to the starboard (or right-hand) side. They each possess a field of illumination of 112½° (Illustration 105, Fig B).

Illustration One Hundred & Five   Approved Navigation Light Layouts

Fig 105B Sidelights

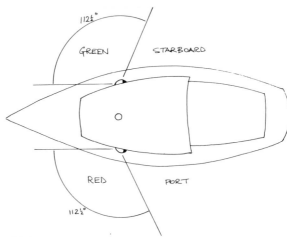

Bi-Colour Lights

Bow mounted Bi-colour Lights are a popular alternative, to sidelights, on boats less than 20m in overall length. Being easier to install, they are preferred - only one set of wires, and a Bi-colour Light takes less power from the battery, than two individual sidelights. They have to be mounted on the centre line of a craft, and as far forward as possible, more often than not on the pulpit. A Bi-Colour Light consists of a single bulb that has an overall illumination angle of 225°. The lens is divided vertically into two, with a green (or starboard) section and a red (or port) section, each having a vector of 112½°. (Illustration 105, Fig C).

Fig 105C Bi-Colour Lights

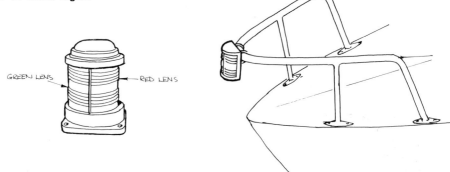

Masthead Lights

(b) The Masthead (or Steaming Light) is a white light mounted at the top of the mast. On smaller motor boats (less than 12m in length) it must be affixed 1m above the side-lights. This distance increases to 2.5m above the sheer of the gunwale, for boats between 12m and 20m in length. The field of illumination is 225° and the unit must be mounted facing forward.

All-Round or Anchor Light

(c) The All-Round (or Signal Light) gives illumination through 360°, and is available in white, red or green. The white version is the most popular on small vessels, where it is often referred to as the Anchor Light, probably because it has to be illuminated at night, when, riding at anchor. On larger vessels, such as fishing boats and other commercial craft, the white, red and green signal lights are all fitted, in order to indicate to other craft the particular activity in which they are involved.

(d) The white Stern Light is fitted as close to the after end of the particular craft, as is possible. It has a field of illumination of 135°, and is mounted so that it is shines directly aft (Illustration 105, Fig D).

Stern Light

Fig 105D Stern Light

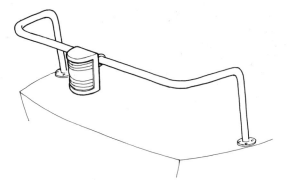

(e) The Tri-Colour Light is popular for sailing craft, less than 20m in overall length. It not only combines the two sidelights, but also the stern light, giving an overall field or illumination angle of 360°, with sectors of 120° red, 120° green and 120° white. It is usually mounted at the top of the mast and units are available 'topped off' with a second, all-round white light, resulting in a combined Tri-Colour/Anchor Light (Illustration 105, Fig E).

Tri-Colour Light

Fig 105E Tri-Colour & Anchor Lights

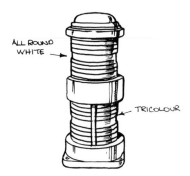

The usual Tri-Colour Light has a single bulb which, although higher in power than a normal bulb, is more efficient than three individual lights, and is a lot easier to wire into the circuit. The combined Tri-Colour/Anchor Light possess two bulbs.

Other External Lights are required to allow mariners to carry out jobs in the dark. For instance, night-time navigation instruments must be illuminated. Larger craft may possess deck walk and cockpit lights, however these are generally small, low power units.

Other External Lighting

An item often common to small and large craft alike is the Spotlight. How a Spotlight is to be deployed depends on whether a boat is used for seagoing or inland waterway cruising. Seagoing vessels may well utilise a Spotlight for identifying buoys, moorings or, in an emergency situation, say, a man (or woman) overboard. Thus, generally, the fitting has a more powerful, restricted width of beam, than is ideal for inland waterway use.

Spotlights

Night-time cruising on the inland waterways is much easier with the provision of a Spotlight, due to the more-often-than-not restricted width of the river, canal or broad. In fact, canal boaters must have a Spotlight in order to navigate a tunnel. Averagely the Spotlight should give a wider spread than that of the 'pencil' beam type more popular for estuary and sea boats.

The amount of illumination Spotlights provide is normally measured in candlepower - which may not be much help to those of us unable to visualise 100,000 candles! Without doubt, the best test of a Spotlight is trial and error, so why not try someone else's? It is worth determining the current a particular unit takes, and as most draw quite heavily on the power supply, they should be only switched on for short periods.

*External
Lighting
Practicalities*

Up until this point in the book, nearly all the electrical items detailed have been below decks. Thus little has been mentioned about preventing water ingress, and the resultant contamination. If and when water comes into contact with electrical equipment, as sure as day follows night, it will corrode and cease to function, after a period of time, be it one week or one year.

It is recommended that the following guidelines are applied to all marine electrical equipment, but more especially externally mounted items:-

(a) Ensure that every fitting is intended for marine use, or has been marinised by the manufacturer.

(b) Mount equipment clear of areas around which water collects, runs away or drips.

(c) Apply a coating of silicone grease or *Vaseline* to all exposed connections, including the insides of plugs and sockets.

(d) Where possible, use tin plated wire for all external wiring.

(e) Incorporate drip loops into the wiring (*See* Illustration 101).

*Thru' Deck
Connectors &
Plug Sockets*

When equipment is mounted externally, the problem arises of how to get power from the inside to the outside, without incurring leaks and possible water damage. Usually the solution is achieved by employing one of two methods. The first is to use a Thru' Deck Plug and Socket, as described in Chapter 7 (*See* Illustration 96), whilst the second is to fit a deck gland (*See* Illustration 96). The advantage of a deck gland is that it can be fitted – and forgotten, whereas plugs and sockets are prone to corrosion at the pins and pin holes. On the other hand, a plug and socket must be fitted where a piece of equipment has to be easily disconnected and reconnected.

**Internal
Lighting**

Despite the different number of (Interior) lights available, most can be divided into two types - incandescent and discharge.

*Incandescent
Lights*

Incandescent Lights have been around for a long time. The first was manufactured in the late 1870s, when it was discovered that if an electric current was passed through a small piece of wire, in a vacuum, the wire heated up and emanated light. Incandescent Lights are commonly used in all applications except, possibly, industrial and office lighting, where discharge lighting is more popular.

Certainly navigation and external lighting utilise incandescent bulbs, because they produce a very small, concentrated light source. The latter is determined by the size of the wire filament heated by the electric current. The benefit of this is that it can easily be reflected, directed and focused, employing mirrors or lenses. These qualities also result in Incandescent Lighting being very suitable for spotlights and torches, as well as any other lights that require to be pinpointed, or shone into a particular area.

An Incandescent Light should give at least one thousand hours life, although over-voltage and excessive switching may cause this figure to decrease.

*Discharge or
Fluorescent
Lights*

Discharge Lights are more usually referred to as Fluorescents, and they work in a different fashion to incandescent lamps. When a large voltage is applied to certain gases, electric current can be made to flow through them, in the form of a discharge. This action causes the gases to radiate light.

Fluorescents, which are the most common Discharge Lights, give a much more even spread of illumination, as it is generated over the whole length of the tube. However, it is a harsher, more clinical light, with a lot of blue/white content. By contrast, incandescent lights tend to give a 'warmer', more homely glow. However various types of Fluorescent are now available that emit slightly different colours of light, some supposedly emulating the qualities of incandescent bulbs.

The major benefit of Fluorescent lighting is its efficiency - it produces, on average, four times as much light-per-watt, of electrical power, as incandescent lights, and two and half times less radiant heat - the latter being the reason that incandescent lights are 'warmer' (Illustration 106).

Illustration One Hundred & Six   Incandescent versus Discharge Lights

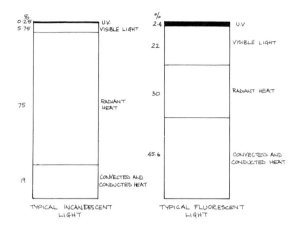

This sketch details the breakdown of the split in the power supplied to Incandescent and Fluorescent Lights. The important figures are the percentages of visible light that each produces - 5.75% for Incandescent and 22% for Fluorescent Lights.

A control circuit is necessary, with all Fluorescent Lights, to commence the discharge and keep it steady, once it has started. In 12V DC units a converter circuit is fitted. This transforms the DC input to the high frequency, alternating output required to allow the discharge to take place.

Unfortunately, these circuits create a couple of problems:-

(a) They are more expensive, as the light is no longer simply a connector and a bulb.

(b) They are electrically quite noisy, so have to be mounted some distance from elec-
tronic equipment, such as radios and depth sounders. In fact electronic gear must be wired on a separate circuit to any Fluorescent Lighting, which also 'pulsate' at the frequency of the supply.

Any increased cost is more than offset by the higher efficiency of Fluorescents and their extended bulb/tube life, which can be as much as five times that of incandes-
cent bulbs. In weighing up the pros and cons of Incandescent vis-a-vis Discharge lighting, each has its good and bad points, and any selection probably comes down to the style, size and colour of a particular fitting, rather than its electrical properties!

*Pros & Cons,
Incandescent
& Discharge*

A fairly new development of Incandescent Lighting is the Tungsten Halogen Lamp. In these a tungsten filament runs in a quartz envelope that contains halogen gas (usually bromine). This arrangement results in improved light output over the conventional incandescent lights - up to three or four times the Lumens per watt. They must be worth considering, as an alternative to fluorescent lights, for, although they are more expensive to purchase, they have a considerably increased bulb life. They are now available as 12V 10W lamps, with a 'domestic' size bayonet cap, so can be fitted in place of the commonplace incandescent bulbs, compared to which they are much less noisy and very efficient.

Tungsten Halogen bulbs should not be handled, without using a doubled-up tissue or clean, soft cloth, as the grease of one's fingers may well damage the delicate quartz construction of the bulb, when it heats up.

*Tungsten
Halogen
Lamps*

Lighting installation depends on the particular type of fitting, although most have screw terminal connections, similar to 3 pin, mains plugs. Fastening lights to deckheads or bulkheads normally requires drilling and screwing, and possibly, jig-sawing/routing if the unit has to be recessed.

Bulbs are always marked with the working voltage (ie 12V DC, 24V DC, 240V AC, *et al),* and also may have the power rating marked (ie 20W, 50W, and so on). With these two values, the current required can be worked out (as set out in Chapter 2, wherein it was

*Lighting
Installation*

stated that (Power (W) = Voltage (V) x Current (A), or, as required here, Current = Power ÷ Voltage). This is necessary to determine the requisite fuses and wiring, for a particular lighting circuit.

Incandescent bulbs can be tested by measuring their resistance (approximately 10 ohms, or less, is typical), but this method does not apply to fluorescent bulbs.

At this point it is apposite to show how to wire a - 'switch on here, switch off there' type of circuit. An everyday, domestic example of this installation is to be found at the top and bottom of an everyday staircase, to enable the landing light to be switched on or off, whether on the ground or first floor (Illustration 107). This is assuming a reader doesn't live in a bungalow!

Illustration One Hundred & Seven   Two-Way Switching
(or Switch On Here, Switch Off There)

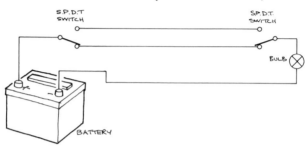

For details of the SPDT (Single Pole Double Throw Switch), See Chapter 7, Illustration 97,

A Typical Installation

When fitting out or rewiring a boat, the following should be kept in mind:-

(a) Use fluorescent lighting for the main living areas, as well as the galley and toilet compartments, where reliable, bright, 'even' lighting is needed.

(b) In the main living area, consider backing-up fluorescent lighting with a couple of small, recessed or bulkhead incandescent lights. These allow crew to be up-and-about, down below, without fluorescent lights being switched on, which might well spoil a helmsman's night vision.

(c) The latter point reminds one to suggest that it is worth considering purchasing a night vision, red light for mounting in the cockpit, or just inside the companionway, allowing unimpaired night 'eyes'. An inexpensive alternative is to give the lens of an old torch a 'once over' with a red paint spray.

(d) Do not assume that the best place for a light is in the middle of the deckhead. Consider the layout of any cabin and, for instance, which way round the crew lounge, during their spare time (What spare ...!). And which way round is meant to indicate that it is necessary to ascertain if the crew usually have their head to the bow or stern bulkhead of a particular cabin.

(e) Resist going OTT in respect of interior lighting - it is surprising how soon that which appears to be a dimly lit area, proves to be acceptable with use. On the other hand, save money, and torch batteries, by having a small, but thoughtfully placed number of fittings.

Fresh Water Pumps

Manual Water Pumps

Most modern craft have an electric pump fitted in the freshwater system. There are basically three types, the:-

(a) Manually 'switched' System. They are the simplest and cheapest choice, often found on smaller boats, with only one or two water points.
In fact, a small Pump-cum-foot switch will suffice on most craft with only one outlet. The faucet may well be simply a bent piece of stainless steel tubing. To turn the water on, press the foot pump, which forces water out of the pipe. Of course it is not necessary to use a foot switch. Any manual arrangement, such as a lever or plunger will do, but generally foot switches are preferred, as they leave both hands free, and are less obtrusive.

Electric Water Pumps

(b) Microswitch System. These are suitable for boats with more than one water outlet, and are a small Electric Pump, with a special tap at each water point. The latter resemble domestic units, and turn the water flow on and off in the same manner. The difference is that inside each tap is a microswitch (a tiny electrical switch). As the tap is turned on, as well as opening the tap water valve, the switch closes, activating the pump, thus causing the water to flow (Illustration 108, Fig A).

Illustration One Hundred & Eight   Drinking Water Systems

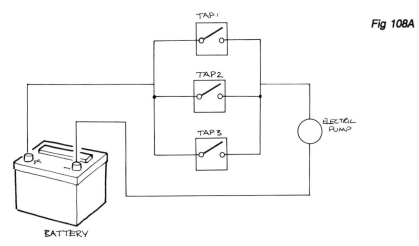

Fig 108A

A typical system in which the (three) taps, each with its microswitch, are wired in parallel with the others. This is so that the operation of any one of the taps results in the battery being directly connected to the pump.

(c) Pressure Switch System. Larger boats, with a lot of water points, are best served by a Pressure Switched Electric Pump system. Standard domestic taps can be used, combined with a special pump which, unlike the previously detailed, manually operated pumps, automatically starts up, when a tap is turned on, and stops, when the tap is turned off (Illustration 108, Fig B).

Pressure Switched Electric Pump

Fig 108B

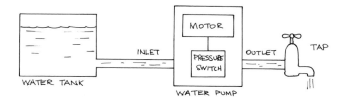

A simplified installation drawing, complete with a water tank, pump and tap. The pressure switch in the pump measures the pressure at the inlet pipe (water tank) and compares it with the pressure at the outlet pipe (tap). The action of turning on the tap causes the pressure, at the outlet, to drop below that at the inlet. This occasions the pressure switch to close and turn the motor on, which pumps water, from the tank to the tap. When the tap is turned off, there is nowhere for the water being pumped to go, which results in a build-up of pressure, at the outlet pipe. When this exceeds the pressure at the inlet, the pressure switch opens, and cuts off the power to the motor. The motor remains inactive as long as outlet pressure exceeds the inlet pressure, that is until the tap is turned on again.

The latter system is easier to install, if more expensive, and is supposed to be more reliable than, the 'manually' microswitched electric pump. However, a drawback is that if there is a badly dripping tap, or the plumbing has a large leak, the pump will turn on for a few seconds, every now and again. Incidentally, anyone who has overnighted on a boat with this problem, and is unfortunate enough to have the pump mounted beneath their bunk, will readily appreciate that to save a sleep-interrupted night, it is best to turn the wretched thing off - at the fuse panel! Mind you, it is usual that this type of installation will also have an accumulator, which evens out pressure pulses and 'soaks' up slight increases, and decreases, in line-pressure.

Electric Fans

Generally boats are fairly confined and are not renowned for adequate ventilation - leading to an increasing number of modern-day craft being fitted with one or more Electric Fans. Most marine Fans are used for extraction from compartments, such as the galley and toilet, as well as the engine room. Some Fans are wired to allow the selection of 'extract' or 'blow'.

A Fan's capacity to extract/blow air is usually quoted as cubic feet, or cubic metres, per hour. Say a Fan is rated as having a capacity of 1350 ft³/hour, and the galley is 7½ ft long, 6ft wide and 6ft high, then:-

The volume of the galley = 7½' x 6' x 6'
= 270ft³

As the fan can extract 1350ft³/hour, the number of times the air in the galley is replaced, every hour, is:-

1350 ft³/hour ÷ 270 ft³   = 5 times

Put another way, if the galley stove burnt toast one morning, the Fan would take a 1/5 of an hour, or 12 minutes, to get rid of the smell.

To achieve maximum efficiency from a Fan, the air being blown/extracted   must have an unimpeded path. For this reason they are usually mounted to a craft's deckhead, so extracted air can be expelled directly from a ventilator (Illustration 109).

Ilustration One Hundred & Nine   Fans

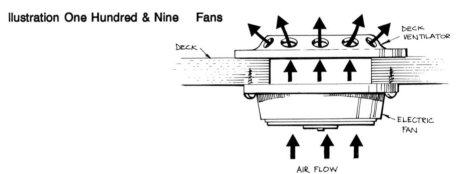

As well as ensuring that extracted air can escape, without hindrance, it is important that fresh supplies, from outside, can easily flow into a craft, if only to replace the extracted air. To facilitate this, leave open a window, hatch or door, whilst the Fan is running.

When selecting a Fan, first calculate the volume of air that has to be extracted, as outlined in the 'Galley example'. A useful 'ventilation rule of thumb' is that an area should be totally ventilated four times every hour. With this empirical figure to hand, to calculate the capacity of the Fan required, multiply the volume of air by four.

For instance, if a toilet compartment has a volume of 180 ft³, then the Fan capacity must be greater than:-

180 ft³ x 4 = 720 ft³/hour

As well as a Fan having the necessary capacity, it must not 'overtax' a craft's battery when it is deployed. Usual current ratings range from 0.1A to 10A, or more. Typical 'capacity to power consumption' ratios are that a 2000 ft³/hour unit draws 5W, whilst a 10,000 ft³/hour Fan requires 50W.

Solar Fans

Solar powered Fans have a built-in solar panel that provides the necessary power to run the unit, during daylight hours. They are useful, but rarely possess very large extraction capacities to cope with other than the requirements of a small compartment. If fitting a Fan (or fans) to combat night-time condensation, then solar units are of no use. That is unless they have built-in rechargeable batteries (as some do), which can be charged during daylight hours, and used to power the Fan at night - *sans sun!*

It is desirable to 'force ventilate' or aspirate both the engine and crowded, 'busy' battery compartments. The latter is especially necessary during charging, when there is the greatest risk of a hydrogen gas build-up - the discharge of a large quantity of highly inflammable gas presenting a very great risk of an explosion. (Illustration 110).

Battery/
Engine
Compartment
Extraction

Illustration One Hundred & Ten   Battery & Engine Compartment Extraction

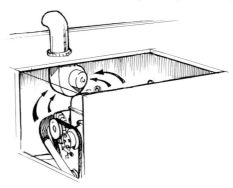

Instead of separately 'switching', why not organise matters so that the fan is wired into the ignition switch, so that venting is not forgotten?
It must be remembered that the DC motors used to 'power' Fans can be an 'excellent' source of electrical arcing (or sparks). Thus where, for instance, venting a battery compartment, or petrol powered engine room, only a gas or flame-proof unit should be fitted.

On larger craft, the ability to quickly and easily haul in the anchor is a requirement most conveniently facilitated with the provision of an electric powered Anchor Winch. This is basically an electric motor, rather similar to an engine starter motor (Illustration 111).

Anchor
Winches

Illustration One Hundred & Eleven   Anchor Winches

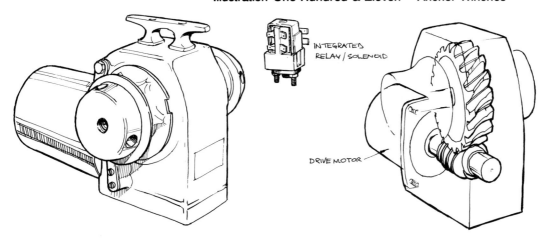

Anchor Winches are usually geared to operate at low speeds. This is so the maximum torque can be applied, in order to lift the weight of an anchor, at a controllable speed - similar to changing down to a car's 1st gear, to climb a steep hill. The lifting power of Anchor Winches can vary from 150lbs to over 2000lbs. As the electrical power required is usually between 500W and 2000W, they represent a substantial current drain on a 12V, or 24V, battery. Due to the high currents, Anchor Winches normally have an integral solenoid, or relay, that allows a small, low current switch to operate the mechanism, similar to a starter motor. (*See* Chapter 6, Illustration 60 - Starter Motors, and Chapter 7, Illustration 98 - Relays).

The speed at which Winches are able to lift an anchor varies, depending on the power of the unit, and the weight of the anchor, but typical values are between 25ft and 80ft per minute. Most have motors that are reversible, so that the Winch can be used to release the anchor, as well as hauling it up.

Winch Wiring
Requirements

The most important matter to establish, when considering the installation of a deck mounted Anchor Winch, is the size of cable required to carry the current necessary to 'power' the motor, safely and without the risk of burning out the wires. The calculation is similar to those set out in Chapter 2, whilst the specific cable can be chosen from the Wire Rating Table in Chapter 7 (*See* Illustration 89, Fig A).

Electric Bilge
Pumps

Electric Bilge Pumps should not be relied upon to 'save the day', in the event of a craft having a 'sinking' leak. A pump capable of keeping a craft afloat, in this situation, would draw so much current that a normal battery would only last a short time, before going flat. Owners who wish to be able to pump out a boat, when it is sinking, should invest in a pump that is driven from the boat's engine, or a separate power source. One other, non-electrical footnote is to ensure a one-way, non-return valve is fitted in the outlet pipe of the system. Why? Well, submersible pumps, for one, can siphon back - filling the boat up! Incidentally, it is a well-known fact that the most efficient Bilge Pump, for a sinking ship... is a frightened man, with a large bucket!

Without doubt, an Electric Bilge Pump is the most 'labour saving' method of keeping a craft's bilges dry, under normal conditions. As a result, there is a wide choice of units available, for both 12V and 24V systems, but they generally fall into two categories:-

Submersible
Pumps

(a) Submersible Pumps. These units can only work if the lower body is submerged. Once under water, the centrifugal impeller excavates, typically, between 2 and 20 gallons of water per minute, depending on the size and power consumption of the particular Pump. Not only are they, generally, the least expensive units available, but they offer very low current consumption, when compared to other Pumps. For most applications, submersibles are ideal, but they must be placed at the very lowest section of the bilges, and be mounted upright, on as flat a surface as possible. Their 'bottom of hull' location results in the tendency to forget them - out of sight, out of mind - so it is worth purchasing a robust unit (Illustration 112).

Illustration One Hundred & Twelve   Submersible Electric Bilge Pumps

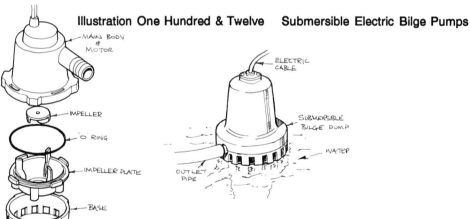

Apart from normal maintenance problems, caused by a damaged impeller or, occasionally, the seal and 'O' ring, the usual bother, and thus disillusion, associated with Submersibles, is their propensity to blow fuses, for no apparent reason. This is especially prevalent when they are fitted in conjunction with an automatic float switch.

To cope with the mechanical difficulties why not pack a spare of each? To deal with the electrical problem, read on!

Self-priming
Pumps

(b) Self-priming Pumps. As they are able to prime themselves, and draw water up a pipe, they can be mounted distant from the bilges, in a dry area. Naturally the suction pipe must be placed in the bottom of the bilges. Some Self-priming Pumps require a filter, fitted to the end of the inlet pipe, or in the pump itself, to stop solids from damaging the 'workings'.

Flexible Vane
& Diaphragm
Self-priming
Pumps

Broadly speaking there are two main types of Self-priming Pumps - Flexible Vane

(Illustration 113, Fig A) and Diaphragm (Illustration 113, Fig B). Flexible Vane Units are the cheaper of the two and can pump more water per minute, than Diaphragm Pumps, although they are noisier and require more current.

Illustration One Hundred & Thirteen   Self-Priming Pumps

Fig 113A   Flexible Vane

These pumps can only be run, whilst 'dry', for a few seconds. This weakness is often compensated for by their being plumbed-in with a header tank.

Fig 113B   Diaphragm

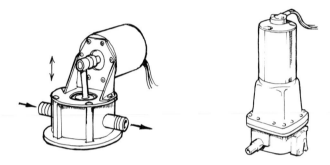

In comparison with a Flexible Vane unit, the Diaphragm Pump can run 'dry' for quite long periods, without damage.

Float Switches

As most boat owners wish to have peace of mind, when their craft is left unattended, a method of automatically switching a bilge pump on and off, had to be devised. The solution was to employ a Float Switch, wired to the pump, which senses when the bilge water has reached a critical level, and switches the 'thing' on (Illustration 114).

Illustration One Hundred & Fourteen   Float Switches

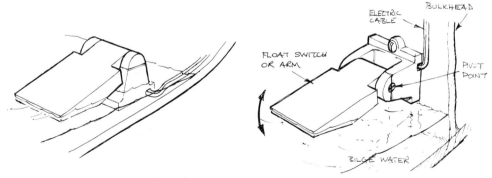

The main body, or arm, of the Float Switch is able to pivot up and down and is designed to float on water. Inside the Float Switch is a ball of mercury that rolls between two points, depending on the angle of the float switch body. It is designed so that when the Float Switch moves above the horizontal, the ball of mercury rolls down, until it touches two electrical connections. This forms a circuit between them, and so operates the switch, and 'fires up' the bilge pump. As soon as the Float Switch arm moves below the horizontal, the mercury ball rolls away from the electrical connections, opening up the switch, which turns off the pump.

A Float Switch also keeps the bilges dry, whilst cruising, without having to remember to continually check 'below the boards'. However, for the Float Switch and bilge pump to operate, when a boat is moored, and presumably with the electrics switched off, requires wiring the pair to the battery, 'upstream' of or between the battery and the main isolator switch (Illustration 115).

Illustration One Hundred & Fifteen   'Upstream' Wiring of the Bilge Pump (& Float Switch)

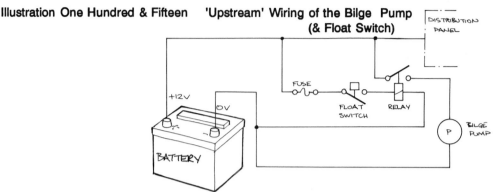

It is vital that the bilge pump circuit is fused, as it is better to return to a boat with brimming bilges, than a burnt-out-craft due to an electrical-fault-triggered-fire.

The life and reliability of a Float Switch can be significantly increased by fitting a relay in order to activate the bilge pump motor. This is due to the relay absorbing a certain amount of start-up current, a 'demand kick' that often causes damage to switch contacts (Illustration 116, Fig A).

Illustration One Hundred & Sixteen   Bilge Pump Circuitry

Fig 116A   Mechanical Switching

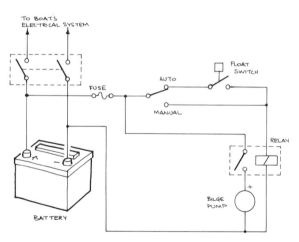

Electric Float Switches

An alternative, if much costlier option to the mechanical Float Switch, is an electronic unit (that is if one unquestionably trust electronics!). These work by sensing the capacitance between two pieces of metal located on the device. When the bilge water rises and covers them, the capacitance between the metal strips changes. The circuitry 'perceives' this change and turns on a solid state switch. It is maintained, by their manufacturers, that solid state, or electronic, switches are better suited to the hostile, marine environment than mechanical switches. Most are guaranteed for 100,000, or more operations.

Installation of an Electronic (bilge pump) Switch is slightly more complicated, than that of a mechanical unit, as it has three connections. Two of these lead to the +12V and 0V of the battery, providing power to the circuitry in the switch, and must be constantly coupled to the battery. The third link is the switched connection, wired to the bilge pump (Illustration 116, Fig B).

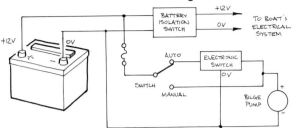

Fig 116B   Electronic Switching

As well as having a float switch, it is common practice to fit a Switch Panel, to allow the bilge pump to be switched on and off manually, as well as automatically (Illustration 117).

Bilge Pump Switch Panel

Illustration One Hundred & Seventeen   Bilge Pump Switch Panels

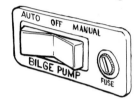

These panels usually consist of a SPDTS (Single Pole Double Throw Switch - See Chapter 7, Illustration 97) that 'turns' on the power, either directly to the pump (manual) or via the float switch (automatic). Some panels incorporate a fuse for the pump, as well as a small light, to indicate when the pump is working.

When selecting pumps and switches:-
(a) Always choose a switch that can easily handle the necessary current required by the pump. For instance, a 5A pump should have a switch that is rated at 1½ times that figure, or 7.5A.
(b) Invest in a reputable manufacturer's unit, able to cope with normal bilge water intake, and then fit a large, manual pump, for emergencies!

A last point to consider, in respect of inductive circuits, is that large, 'start-up' voltages, and power surges, can damage switches, as can 'shut-down' voltages. Oh dear! Switches especially at risk are those used in pump circuits, such as bilge and freshwater systems. To cure the problem is simplicity itself. Fit a suitable diode, the right way round, across the positive and negative supply of the motor (Illustration 118).

Induction Circuit Switch Damage

Illustration One Hundred & Eighteen   Induction Circuit Switch Damage

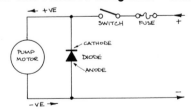

The cathode must be connected to the positive supply. The diode can be located at, say, the switch, if so required, just so long as the 'spirit' of the circuit is followed. Almost any rectifier diode will suffice, as long as it has a reverse voltage rating of at least 50V, thus allowing a sufficient safety margin for a 12V, or 24V, system. Since the diode is not normally conducting, only absorbing the short, inductive spike generated during switch off, the current rating need not be as high as that of the motor. A 1A diode would allow a very reasonable safety margin, for most applications. When purchasing a diode, state the current and voltage requirements. It should preferably be wire-ended, not stud-mounted, for ease of connection, and if any doubt, request the supplier to detail which end is the cathode. Fittting it the wrong way round will blow a fuse, and maybe the diode.

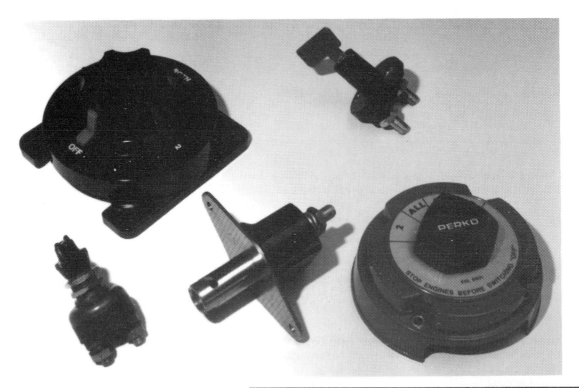

CHAPTER NINE

ELECTRONIC EQUIPMENT

More and more reasonably priced electronic equipment is becoming available, for smaller and smaller boats, but to give detailed information is outside the scope of this book. The aim of this Chapter is to set-out a brief overview of the type of apparatus most commonly installed, with an outline of the requisite maintenance.

Basically, Speed Logs measure boat speed, as well as distance travelled. In fact, now that most manufacturers produce microprocessor controlled log's, the modern-day range of functions may include average speed, a re-setable trip log, a race-timer, stopwatch and other speed, time and distance related information, at the press of a button.

Speed Log

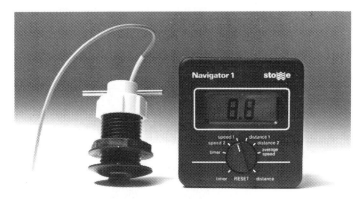

With acknowledgements to Stowe Marine Equipment Ltd.

These Logs work by counting the number of pulses produced by a submerged transducer. The transducer, which comes in various guises, rotates as the water flows past. Every time it rotates, an electrical pulse is produced - as the boat's speed increases, so does the number of times the transducer rotates, per second. By counting the number of pulses (in a second), the boat's speed is calculated. Once the speed has been determined, it is child's-play for the microprocessor to work out the distance travelled, the average speed, or any other function.

There are basically three different types of log transducer:-

Trailing Transducers

(a) The Trailing Transducer. This evolved from the mechanical type of Log, the business end of which was chucked over the side and trailed behind the boat. It is usually fitted with about 10m or more of cable. This allows the impeller to be clear of the craft's wash, to avoid inaccurate readings. As the transducer moves through the water, the fins cause part of the body to spin (Illustration 119, Fig A).

Illustration One Hundred & Nineteen   Speed Logs

Fig 119A   Trailing Transducer

Inside the transducer body is a small reed switch, similar to the switch inside a relay. A magnet, embedded in the part of the transducer that spins, causes the switch to open and then close, every time the transducer rotates. The Log applies a voltage across the reed switch and, as it closes, senses the current that flows through the transducer. The cable has two wires connected to the Log.

This type of transducer is very accurate, it needs no calibration, when installed, and its immunity to electrical noise is good.

Paddle-wheel Transducers

(b) Paddle-wheel Transducers. They are mounted thru' the hull and are intended for permanent installation. They work by having a small rotating paddle-wheel, which has a magnet in one or more of the paddles. Every time the paddle-wheel rotates, the magnet passes close to the transducer body (Illustration 119, Fig B).

Fig 119B   Paddle-wheel Transducer

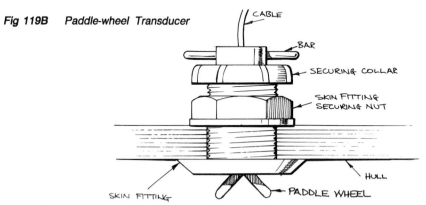

A typical thru' hull Paddle-wheel Transducer. They are prone to picking up flotsam, as well as algae. To counter this and facilitate cleaning, they are designed to be fairly easily drawn-up inside a boat, after which the blanking plug must be quickly placed in the skin fitting - to stop the water pouring in! Once the transducer has been removed, it can be cleaned in white or methylated spirits, and brushed off with an old toothbrush. The rubber 'O' ring, that stops the water from seeping in, should be lubricated with silicone grease, or Vaseline. The paddle-wheel must spin freely, when flicked or blown. To increase the interval between cleaning, it is worth carefully applying a very thin coat of antifouling paint to, or smearing sterntube grease to the paddle- wheel. Either action should keep marine growth at bay, for a longer period, but care must be taken that either measure does not interfere with the paddle-wheel's rotation.

Older transducers of this type have a small coil of wire mounted in them and, as the magnet passes the coil, a small current is induced into the coil, which can be sensed by the Log.

Newer transducers have a 'Hall Effect' switch fitted, which 'turns on', as the magnet passes, and off, as soon as the magnet has passed. These units can be recognised by the three wires required, two of which provide power to the transducer (from the Log) to supply the 'Hall Effect' switch circuit, and a third wire which sends the pulses back to the Log. They are immune to most electrical noise but are, arguably, slightly less reliable than the older, coil pick-up units. On the other hand, 'coil' transducers are more prone to electrical noise interference, due to the small currents produced by the instrument. In fact, if they are badly installed, on an electrically 'noisy' boat, the log may well record erratic speeds, even when the craft is stationary!

'Hall Effect' Switches

Correct installation of Paddle-wheel Transducers is important, due to the proximity of the hull. Different hull shapes have varying effects on the water that flows across them. Any protrusions in the underwater contours can cause a disturbance, which may effect the readings delivered by the paddle-wheel. It is mandatory that the transducer should be mounted clear of the depth sounder transducer, as well as any other skin fittings that might cause an interruption to the water flow. However, even if the transducer is ideally situated, it may well need to be calibrated for the hull shape. This involves cruising over a measured distance and then adjusting the log, so that it measures the correct distance on the return trip.

(c) Ultrasonic Transducers. They use the Doppler effect, which 'everybody knows' is the reason why police sirens appear to change in frequency, as they speed up to - and past a listening bystander.

Ultrasonic Transducers

The transducer transmits a pulse of ultrasonic sound aimed, at the sea-bed, which is then reflected back by the bottom. By comparing the transmit frequency to the received frequency, the speed of the boat can be calculated. These instruments tend to be fitted to larger craft and are more reliable than other units, having no moving parts. However, the thin film of water that moves with the boat, builds up, as the speed increases, and can cause inaccuracies.

A fairly new type of Sonic Transducer has recently been released. This consists of two sensors, mounted about one metre apart, and is an economical proposition for small craft. Both sensors transmit and receive ultrasonic signals, and the time taken for these to travel between the sensors, in both directions, is recorded. That measurement varies with speed and so, from the timings, a value of the boat's speed can be calculated. A typical installation is sketched in Illustration 119, Fig C.

Sonic Transducers

Fig 119C Sonic Transducer

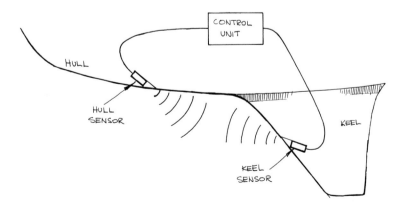

Depth or
Echo
Sounders

Gone are the days of throwing a weighted, knotted rope over the side with which to measure the depth of water. Modern-day Depth Sounders, or Echo Sounders as they are also titled, are probably the most common electronic equipment fitted to leisure craft.

With acknowledgements to Stowe Marine Equipment Ltd.

Depth Sounders operate by sending a pulse of ultrasonic sound to the sea-bed, and then timing how long it takes for this to be reflected back to the transducer. Using the fact that sound waves in water travel approximately 1ft every 0.2ms (millisecond), the Unit is able to calculate the distance from the sea-bed.

As well as providing the depth, in feet, metres, or, in some cases, fathoms, most modern units have a deep and shallow alarm, display depth trends (increasing or decreasing), and have an anchor-watch facility. The shallow alarm is very useful as an audible warning to the helmsman. The deep alarm, used in conjunction with the shallow alarm, can be used as a navigation aid for following the sea-bed contours, or indicating when to take a fix (Illustration 120).

Illustration One Hundred & Twenty   A Depth Sounder Fix

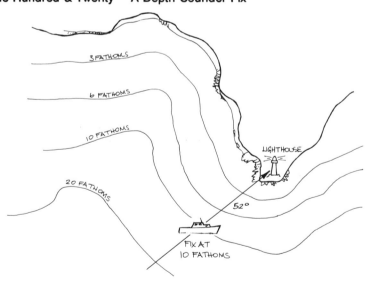

Depth trends, when available, are an attempt to supply the user with an indication of the change in previous readings, so that the sea-bed gradients may be logged - information that can be used for navigation purposes.

Incidentally, the anchor-watch facility guards against the 'pick' being dislodged, or dragging, and the boat subsequently drifting. As soon as the facility is selected, the sounder's micro-processor monitors the average depth of the sea-bed. If a change of more than a few feet is recorded, within one minute, the buzzer sounds. The exact figures are worked out so that changes in the tide, or normal bottom variations, do not set off the buzzer - clever these Chinese!

Nowadays, most depth sounders sport Digital Displays, but a few Analogue units are still sold. The most popular Analogue instrument heads have a rotating flasher assembly, consisting of a motor which rotates a small arm with an LED (Light Emitting Diode), or neon tube, attached to its end. As the arm rotates past the zero mark, a high powered pulse of ultrasonic energy is transmitted towards the sea-bed. This signal hits the bottom and a small echo signal is bounced back. As this is detected by the sounder, it flashes the light. Since the arm has been rotating, whilst the pulse travels to and from the sea-bed, the LED/neon illuminates at a different place on the dial, for different depths (Illustration 121).

Digital Displays

Analogue Displays

Illustration One Hundred & Twenty One   Analogue Depth Sounder Pulses

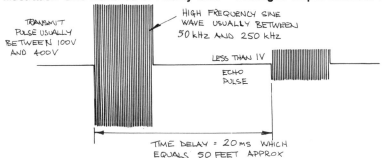

Because of their moving parts, Analogue units are generally less reliable than Digital sounders. The motor that rotates the arm uses quite a lot of current, and thus power consumption is usually greater. In addition, they are bulkier than Digital instruments because the dial has to be big enough to be easily read.

Fish Finder/Depth Recorders are a more sophisticated, complex version of the Depth Sounder. This device carries out greater analysis of the signals it receives, which are displayed on an LCD (Liquid Crystal Display), or 'television' screen. The 'show' is a rolling plot of the sea-bed, with any shoals of fish indicated at the depth they are swimming.
　In the USA the market for these instruments is so large that their cost is not much more than the traditional Depth Sounders. However, in the United Kingdom and Europe they have yet to really catch on, even though they give a much clearer indication of depth. For the average boat owner, their only overriding advantage is that the additional visual information might be used to find the best anchorage, or possibly, for selecting the most suitable type of anchor to use - assuming a craft has more than one anchor.

Fish Finders

Installation of Depth Sounders (Illustration 122, Fig A) involves fitting an instrument head and transducer. The latter is made from a special crystal which vibrates when a high frequency, electrical signal is applied. This vibration emits ultrasonic sound which travels to the sea-bed, and back. For the best performance, the transducer should be mounted thru' the hull, in the same way as a log's paddle-wheel. Incidentally, both depth and log transducers should be mounted as close to the craft's centre line as is possible and, depending on the hull configuration, in the position shown in Illustration 122, Fig B.

Depth Sounder Installation

Illustration One Hundred & Twenty Two   Depth Sounder Installation

Fig 122A   Method 1

The best performance is obtained by fixing the tender/transducer head in an angled wooden block, fibreglassed in place, to stop the ingress of water.

Method 2

Ensures a good performance, but creates a disturbance in the water's flow past the hull, so the transducer should be faired into the bottom with fibreglass.

Method 3

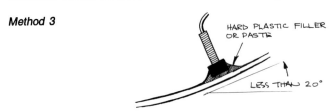

An alternative solution, that does not involve making a hole thru' the hull, is to bond the transducer to the hull, using a hard, plastic based filler, or paste.

Method 4

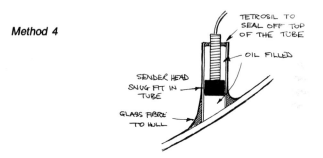

The best method, not requiring a thru' hull hole, is to mount the transducer in a tight-fitting, oil-filled tube. This allows the transducer to be mounted vertically, which Method 3 does not.

Installation methods 3 and 4, which do 'degrade' the unit's performance, should be used by owners who cannot bear the thought of drilling yet another hole in the hull of their boat. However, both should only be used for GRP vessels, with a material thickness of 12.5mm (1/2"), or less.

Method 5

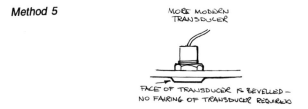

The latest transducer's require the least installation work!

Fig 122B

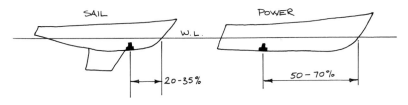

This sketch shows the best, average, fore and aft hull position for a Transducer to be fitted to sail and motor powered craft. To gain the most accurate readings, and allow for the draught of a craft, the Transducer should be positioned as close to the centre line of the hull as is possible.

The Depth Sounder instrument head must be mounted as far away from any radio receiving equipment and compasses as is possible. This is because the circuitry necessary to produce the high frequency depth signal is very similar to radio transmitter circuitry. In fact most Depth Sounders work in the same frequency range as long wave radio stations. All equipment that produces high frequency signals radiates a lot of electrical 'noise'. This may be picked up on a radio receiver, and heard by the listener, as irritating clicks or humming. They also generate small magnetic field fluctuations around the equipment, which can effect compasses, if placed too close. This noise problem is not just limited to the instrument head. The cable to the transducer should be routed away from other wires and cables, as it also radiates electrical noise, which might be picked up by other, adjacent cables.

Wind Instruments

It goes without saying that it is imperative for yachtsmen to know the wind's strength, or speed, and in which direction it is blowing. The modern Wind Instruments are, compared to logs and sounders, quite expensive. However, most offer a level of accuracy greater than the average cruising yachtsmen requires.

All Wind Instruments consist of an instrument head, and a transducer mounted at the top of the mast (Illustration 123).

Illustration One Hundred & Twenty Three   Wind Instruments

Fig 123A   The Masthead Transducer

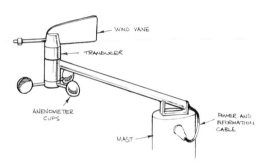

The vane is blown so that it points into the wind. Attached to the vane, inside the body of the transducer, is a variable resistor (or pot). This device outputs a voltage that varies in relation to the wind angle. This voltage is fed to the instrument head, where it can be measured and the wind angle calculated. Other methods for measuring wind angle exist, but generally consist of a sensor, producing a varying voltage, or voltages, relative to the wind direction.

The anemometer cups are rotated by the wind, and their number of revolutions per second is directly proportional to the wind speed. A sensor in the transducer produces an electrical pulse for every revolution - in the same way as the paddle-wheel transducer of a speed log measures boat speed. These pulses are counted and the wind speed calculated.

Fig 123B   The Display Head

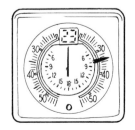

The Display is, almost always, a combined digital and analogue unit, with a needle indicating the wind direction, and a digital display of the wind speed - usually an LCD (Liquid Crystal Display).

Wind
Instrument
Installation

Installing Wind Instruments is usually more complicated than the fitting of logs or sounders. The transducers are subject to considerable environmental stress during their life - a typical unit may spin some 100 million revolutions per year, be subject to hours of direct sunlight and sub-zero temperatures, 'bucket-fulls' of rainwater and sea spray, and even be used as a perch by seagulls. If, for no other reason, they should be taken down and checked, at least once a year, and preferably removed for the winter months. If either the wind vane or anemometer cups appear stiff to turn, then their bearings may require oiling, or replacing. In this case, contact the manufacturer and request they do the job, or dismantle the unit for a DIY job.

The better-engineered transducers have a mounting block for ease of securing to the top of a mast. This allows the unit to be easily attached, or removed, from the block, for servicing or winter lay-up. The wiring to the transducer generally consists of a single four, five or six core cable, depending on the type of wind angle sensor. Two of these wires supply the + 12V and 0V power connections to the transducer. The supply may well be fused, in the instrument head, which should be checked if the instrument does not measure wind speed or angle. One of the wires will be the wind speed signal connection, whilst the remaining one, two or three wires will be those for the wind angle signals.

The cable is affixed all the way to the bottom of the mast, where it must to be routed to the instrument head. This may require drilling a hole through the deckhead and fitting a deck gland, or deck plug and socket (Illustration 123, Fig C).

Fig 123C

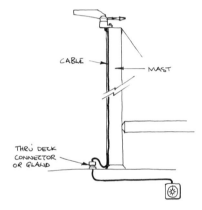

Location
Positioning
Systems

One of the major problems in cruising the oceans (not in too small a boat, I hope!) is determining a craft's exact position. In days of yore this would have been achieved by studying the stars. Nowadays it is made rather easier, using a number of different systems, namely GPS, Transit, Loran and Decca.

Loran &
Decca
Receivers

The Loran and Decca systems use a network of shore-based transmitters. They work by comparing the signals received from two or more transmitters, the difference in the signals pinpointing the position of the receiver. This is an over-simplification, but understanding how each system works, although technically interesting, is of little use to the average boat owner, just so long as they work and supply the necessary 'knowledge'!

Loran, an acronym from 'Long Range Navigation', is an American development which has been around since the Second World War. The latest version, Loran 'C', provides very accurate positional information in nearly all coastal areas of the northern hemisphere. Loran sets can receive information up to 1200 miles from the shore based transmitters. Operation beyond 1200 miles is possible, but with reduced accuracy.

Decca receivers are the British equivalent of Loran, and were also developed in the Second World War. The performance of the two is very similar, with accuracies of plus or minus 50m, under good conditions, although Decca only has a range of 250 miles. Furthermore, Decca's overall coverage is much smaller than Loran, being limited to the British Isles, Western and Northern Europe, the Baltic, Australia, India, Japan, as well as a few other small sectors. Loran, on the other hand, has a coverage that encompasses the United States, Canada, the Pacific and Atlantic Oceans, Europe and the Mediterranean, in addition to many other areas. The number of Decca users is estimated at

140,000, compared to 450,000 dedicated to Loran, and it is expected that Loran will eventually take over from Decca, towards the end of this decade.

As well as providing positional information, most Decca and Loran receivers allow for the proposed course to be entered, using a series of waypoints. The receiver unit then works out where it is, where it wants to go, and provides the helmsman with the heading to steer, for the next waypoint. Other information furnished includes distance to the next waypoint, cross-track error, speed made good, estimated arrival time at the next waypoint, and a number of other position, distance, speed and time-related functions. As yet, I don't think they cook the evening meal, ...but who knows?

With acknowledgements to Navstar Ltd.

Satellite Navigation Systems ('Sat-Nav')

Using satellite signals to calculate a boat's position has been possible since the 1960s. The American 'Transit' satellites, of which there are five, provide boat owners with up to 20 positional fixes, in every 24 hour period. In between each fix, the receiver must calculate its position. To carry this out, boat speed and heading information has to be available, thus electronic log and fluxgate compass also have to be fitted, in order for Sat-Nav to be of any real use. Accuracy between fixes is limited to the precision of the log and compass, and degrades as the time between fixes increases. As positional exactness is no better than plus or minus 100m, navigation using 'Transit' (Sat-Nav) only is not viable for coastal cruising. The benefits of Sat-Nav, over Loran or Decca, becomes apparent when beyond the range of the land-based systems, as it is a worldwide set-up, operating 24 hours a day, rain or shine, for 365 days a year.

Global Positioning Systems

The newest development in Sat-Nav is the Global Positioning System (GPS), developed by the American military, at an estimated cost of $11000 million dollars - so far! It provides accurate and continuous positional information, anywhere in the world. Presently in excess of half of the planned 24 satellites are in orbit, and functioning. As the number increases the accuracy and coverage of the system will increase, and it is expected that GPS will be fully functional by 1992.

A number of manufacturers have already started selling GPS receivers, and the claimed accuracy is to within plus or minus 30m. GPS was designed to supersede the Transit system, which is to be discontinued by December 1996, and is generally expected to become more widely used than the already waning competitors. Prices will undoubtedly fall to those of the Loran and Decca receivers, so it could be worth delaying any planned purchase. But the GPS has a disadvantage, in that it is not so consistent as Loran or Decca. Although its position fixes are, in theory, more accurate, the arrangement 'suffers' very small random errors. With Decca or Loran, a navigator can 'dial-up' a position and cruise to that exact point on the ocean on one day, the next day, and the following day. However, a craft equipped with GPS could easily be 30m, or more, from that same position, from one day to the next.

Installation of 'Sat Nav's'

Installation of Decca, Loran, Transit and GPS systems is no more difficult than fitting a VHF radio. This is hardly surprising, as they are basically radio receivers, with the loudspeakers replaced by a digital display. Furthermore, most of this equipment is sold as a composite, with all the plug-in bits and pieces matched, and in the package.

They all have an aerial/antenna that must be installed externally, and most sail boat owners mount this on the transom, or the masthead, whilst power boat owners fix them to the radar arch, or highest possible point. In both cases the aerial should be as far away as is possible from any VHF or single sideband radio equipment. The aerial is connected to the instrument head by a length of coaxial cable which should be run separately from all other wires. It is preferable that the instrument head is powered on a separate circuit, to additional electronic equipment, in order to avoid any unwanted electric noise effecting its performance.

Autopilots

Autopilots have, in recent years, become a comparatively common 'bolt-on' goodie fitted to leisure boats, and a whole host of different manufacturers offer units. The way in which Autopilots work is basically the same - it is only the size, power and type of steering linkages that vary.

The Autopilot is set a course/heading by the helmsman. Thereon the craft's actual heading is calculated, using an electronic fluxgate compass, which 'passes' this information to the Autopilot. Knowing the required heading and the boat's actual course, the Autopilot's 'brain' calculates which way to turn the rudder.

As steering systems vary from boat to boat, Autopilot manufacturers offer a wide range of steering linkages. The particular one required dictates the type of Autopilot to be used, as does the displacement of a boat.

Tiller & Wheel Pilots

Probably the most popular units are Tiller and Wheel Pilots, which are quite easy to install and can be tackled by the enthusiastic amateur, as long as he or she is 'firmly clutching' the manufacturer's installation instructions (Illustration 124).

Illustration One Hundred & Twenty Four   Autopilots

Fig 124A Tiller Pilot

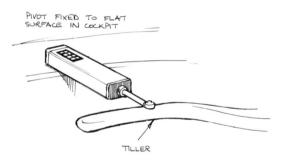

Fig 124B Wheel Pilot

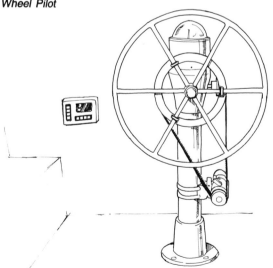

With acknowledgements to Nautech Ltd.

Other Autopilots, with hydraulic linkages, and or 'mated to' sterndrives, are best fitted by professionals, as they can involve complex installation procedures.

Power consumption of Autopilots tends to be higher than other electronic instruments, even the smallest units requiring about 5W - mainly due to the needs of the control motor that positions the steering mechanism. Autopilots 'make-do' with a +12V DC supply. The more sophisticated versions accept information from wind instruments, to allow the pilot to sail to the apparent wind and carry out automatic changing of course, during tacking. Another increasingly popular feature, is the facility to 'send' information from a Decca, Loran or GPS receiver to the Autopilot. Thus a helmsman can enter all the necessary waypoints, into the navigator, which provides the information to the Autopilot, for it to effortlessly and very accurately steer a craft to each of the waypoints, in turn. Soon a boat simply won't require any crew!

Radio Telephones

VHF Radio

The most popular method of boat to boat, and boat to shore, communication is to use a VHF Radio transceiver. These relatively cheap, small and reliable units allow communication between craft, up to 25 miles apart, and communication from boat to shore, over even large distances.

The use of very high frequencies (VHF) means that the signals are less likely to be affected by weather conditions - great for marine use. VHF radios all work at around 160MHz and are usually limited to 25W peak output power. The standard number of channels, more often than not supplied, is fifty-five, where each is a slightly different frequency. To communicate, both radios must be set to the same channel. Certain frequencies are reserved for coastguards, distress calls, weather information, harbour/port operations, and other common usages, therefore not all the channels are available for routine communication between operators.

Single Side Band

Compared to other radio systems, such as Single Sideband, VHF sets are very simple to install, as they do not require any special grounding. The chief consideration is where to mount the aerial/antenna. This should be as high as possible, because the range of VHF communication is limited to objects in its 'line of sight', as detailed in Illustration 125.

Illustration One Hundred & Twenty Five   VHF Radio 'Line of Sight'

The antenna's height effects the range. The signal from Boat A to Boat B will not reach, at a range of 30 miles. In contrast Boats C and D, with taller masts and, thus, higher antennae, are able to communicate up to 40 miles apart.

Another factor worth bearing in mind is to fit the antenna well away from any metal objects and the antennae of Decca/Loran/GPS receivers. The actual radio should be mounted as far from additional electronic instruments (30 cm minimum), and wired separately. The coaxial cable to the antenna must be run separately to and kept at least 10 cm away from any different wiring, as well as signal cables for Depth Sounders and Decca's.

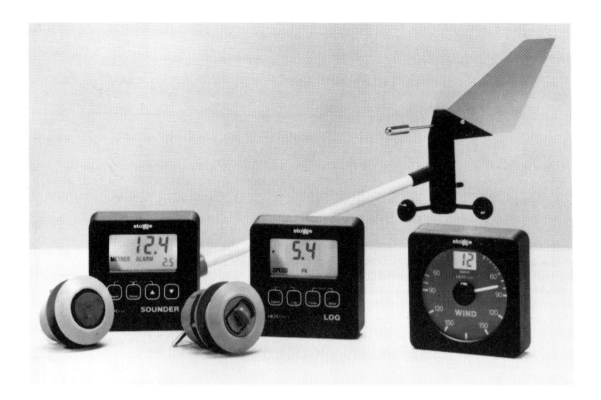

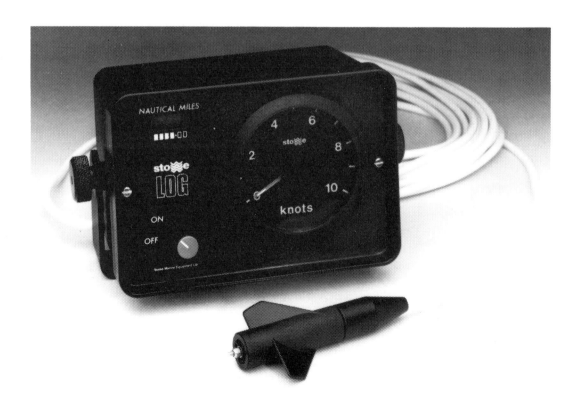

CHAPTER TEN

ELECTRICAL NOISE & SUPPRESSION

Electrical noise consists of high frequency pulses and spikes of electrical energy that combine with the energy produced by a boat's battery and or generator. If it were possible to 'see' the voltage of a craft's electrical system, it would not appear as a 'nice', stable +12V (or +24V) supply, but would appear as sketched in Illustration 126.

Illustration One Hundred & Twenty Six   A 'Sight' of Voltage

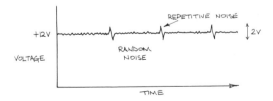

Random electrical noise is a natural phenomenon and always exists, being caused by impure materials that are not uniform. Any substance possesses differences in its chemical and physical construction. These dissimilarities cause varying paths of resistance, which, when a current flows, results in very small voltage fluctuations within the substance itself. The latter is the origin of Random Noise, which can be amplified in electronic equipment (such as radios) to form background hum.

Random Noise

Repetitive Noise

A more irritating manifestation, than random interference, is the very common Repetitive Noise. This nuisance is usually generated by a craft's equipment, and is normally much greater in voltage than random noise. Fortunately, with a little effort, the source, or sources, can be located and suppressed.

Typical creators of noise on boats include:-
(a) Alternators and or dynamos.
(b) Battery chargers and generators.
(c) Inverters.
(d) Propeller shafts.
(e) Any type of electric motor, such as pumps.
(f) Petrol engine ignition systems.
(g) Fluorescent lighting.
(h) Televisions and radar.
(i) Nearly all types of electronic microprocessor controlled instruments, such as logs and echo sounders.

Most noise problems show up as humming, buzzing or crackling, emitting from audio equipment, typically radios. Other noise related problems may not be so easy to identify, but common symptoms are:-
(a) Electronic logs showing a boat speed, when the boat is moored!
(b) Irregular/impossible readings from a depth sounder.
(c) Decca and Loran systems losing their signal, where the reception should be good.
(d) Poor television picture.

Conducted Noise

Random or repetitive electrical noise is conducted or radiated. Conducted Noise travels from the equipment creating it, to the equipment affected, via the boat's wiring.

Radiated Noise

Radiated Noise is transmitted through the air, in much the same manner as radio signals, and is picked up by other equipment, whose circuitry, or wiring, acts as an aerial.

Where 'noise' is a problem, the cause may be determined by turning off each and every piece of equipment, one after the other. As soon as the noise disappears - hey presto, the last item must be the culprit.

Engine Noise

Another very common source of noise is the engine and should the interference cease when it is turned off, then more investigation will be required. If the engine is a diesel unit, and the noise is rhythmic, appearing to speed up or slow down, in concert with the power unit, then the cause is likely to be the alternator, or dynamo.

If a petrol engine is involved, the cause might be the ignition system. To determine whether the dynamo/alternator is at fault, disconnect the fan-belt and run up the engine. If the noise is not apparent, then it must be the generating equipment. Note that removing the fan-belt is safer than disconnecting the output wire of the alternator/dynamo, a course of action that might cause serious damage to either.

Where the Engine Noise is not rhythmic, and appears to be a random crackle or popping, then it could be originating from the propeller shaft, the rotation of the latter causing occasional sparks of static electricity.

Noise Cures

To cure a noise problem, it is necessary to stop it at the source, or at the receiver. The first is the ideal solution, but assumes that the source can be tracked down!

Capacitors

The easiest method of reducing noise, as reduce is the best that can be achieved, is to buy a selection of Capacitors from an electronics shop. Capacitors are extremely high in resistance (more than 1,000,000 ohms) to DC current, but provide a very low resistance path for the high frequency AC current - of noise.

By connecting a Capacitor across the input terminals of the item, that appears to be causing the problem, the noise is given a very low resistance to flow through and back to the equipment (Illustration 127). The noise is commonly said to have been 'shorted out'.

Illustration One Hundred & Twenty Seven   A Capacitor Noise Cure

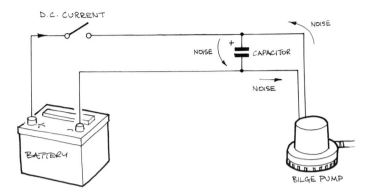

Here the 'culprit' is a bilge pump. The capacitor symbol in the Illustration is shown with a ' + ' at the top. This is because large Capacitors are often polarity conscious, and so the   + ve of the Capacitor must be connected to the + ve supply wire of the equipment. Furthermore some Capacitors are rated for fairly low DC voltages, thus it is necessary to ensure that only Capacitors with working DC voltages of 25V minimum are fitted to + 12V systems, or 40V minimum to + 24V installation. These minimum voltages are necessary to ensure the capacitors continue to work, year in, year out. If the capacitor voltage were too close to the working voltage, the capacitor would eventually fail or, possibly, blow up!

Capacitance is measured in Farads and, in practice, the largest value Capacitors are only 0.1 F (farads). More commonly, Capacitors are measured and referred to in microfarads (uF) - a millionth of a farad. A sensible range of Capacitor values to have handy includes 0.01uF, 1uF, 10uF, 1000uF and 22,000uF. Selection of the right Capacitor, for any particular job, is very much a matter of trial and error, so try one or two different values to see which gives the best results.

Farads

If stopping the noise at the source, with the use of Capacitors, does not work, or is not practical, then the noise must be reduced at the receiver, that is the piece of equipment affected by the noise. This 'receiver' remedy can similarly be effected using Capacitors, or by fitting a device called an Inductor, or Choke, in conjunction with a Capacitor (Illustration 128).

Inductor or Choke

Illustration One Hundred & Twenty Eight   A Capacitor & Choke

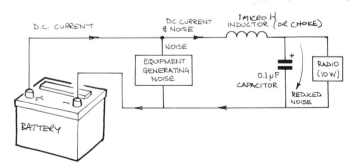

Inductors, or Chokes, are basically coils of wire that offer little resistance to DC current, but resist the flow of AC current. However, having stated this, Inductors do have a higher value of resistance than normal wire and so will dissipate some power. Inductors always have a maximum current rating and it is important that the DC current to flow through them is less than this rating. In the illustration, a radio consumes 10W of power and so takes:-

10W ÷ by 12V = 0.83A

The Inductor should therefore be rated at a minimum of 1A, otherwise, when the current flows, it will get too hot and be damaged.

An Inductor is the opposite to a capacitor - it presents a large   resistance to high frequency AC current, but appears as a very small   resistance to DC current. For this reason it is placed in series with the item of equipment to be suppressed and, in so doing, impedes the high frequency noise. Any significant noise that manages to flow through the Inductor, without being so attenuated that it is unnoticeable, should flow through the 1uF capacitor, never reaching and effecting the equipment.

Henrys

Inductance is measured in 'Henrys' (Well it would be, wouldn't it!). Like capacitors, typical values are normally very small and a selection of 1 micro-Henry (uH) (one millionth of a Henry), 10uH and 100uH Inductors are handy to have available.

Capacitors and inductors, more often than not, simply have wires sticking out from their bodies (Illustration 129). For this reason it is necessary to solder them directly to the equipment terminus. Alternatively, they can be soldered to two lengths of wire, that can then be connected to some crimps.

Illustration One Hundred & Twenty Nine   Fitting Capacitors & Inductors

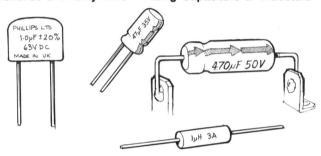

In the section on anodic protection, in Chapter 7, it was shown that electrically connecting a number of metallic objects and skin fittings together, to form a common ground, could, with the use of sacrificial anodes, decrease the chance of galvanic corrosion. This is because all the equipment, connected, or 'bonded', to the common ground, is held at the same potential and so decreases the amount of galvanic action that can take place.

Bonding

Similarly, it is possible to improve the suppression of noise by having a satisfactory Bonding system, as well as a ground with the sea-water, using phosphor-bronze plates mounted through the hull (Illustration 130). If all the metallic objects are connected together, then any radiated noise they pick up will be dissipated to the sea-water ground, thus no voltage differences, or build-up of static, will be able to exist.

Illustration One Hundred & Thirty   A 'Ground', or Equipment Bonding

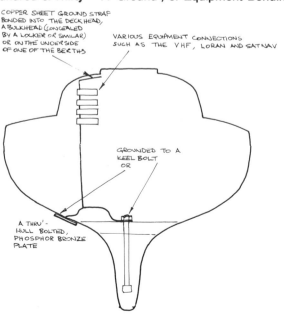

Where a common ground exists, Screened Cables will contain, and short to the ground, any noise radiated from the wires running in the cable. If the Screen is not grounded, then the noise will radiate through the screen into adjacent wires or nearby circuits, possibly causing further noise problems.

Screened Cable

A noise cure, or Filtering, using capacitors, can often be improved by connecting to a bonding system, instead of connecting directly across the +ve and -ve supply, from the battery, as sketched in Illustration 127.

Filtering

Filtering noise to ground, in effect, completely removes it from the electrical system, rather than allowing it an alternative, low resistance, 'away from it all' track. The latter only leaves the noise 'lurking' in the electrical system, from whence it may effect another piece of equipment, fitted at a later date. In other words, by not Filtering noise to ground, the problem is not cured, just hidden. This Filtering of the noise to ground is sketched in Illustration 131.

Illustration One Hundred & Thirty One   Filtering

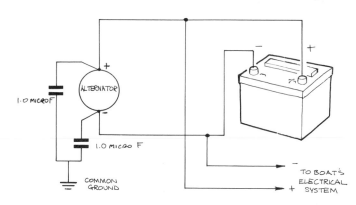

One last word of warning is not to be tempted to use a steel (or any other metal) hull as an earth return. It will cause corrosion, and is strictly 'verboten'.

CHAPTER ELEVEN

FAULT-FINDING

Whenever electrical equipment fails to work, it is an inconvenience, to say the least! If failure occurs whilst afloat, it can prove not only an inconvenience, but downright dangerous. So, if for no other reason, it is advisable that all boat users have some knowledge of the methods involved in fault-finding electrical breakdowns.

The twofold answer to quick and efficient fault-finding is not in owning the most expensive electrical meter available, or even in possessing the greatest knowledge of electrical theory. The first key is simply to take time to think about the circuit at fault, prior to 'diving in' to attempt a quick cure. This may well require supreme self-control, even at the best of times, but more especially if heading towards a storm-tossed shore, in a gale, with the engine dead - or maybe when motoring at full steam-ahead, in the general direction of a pair of enormous canal lock-gates. Understandably really that restraint could go overboard! The second 'must' is to ensure that the test equipment is reliable and correctly set up. Remember the Irish* wheel-tapper who sent hundreds of coaches to the repair sheds - only to discover he had a cracked hammer!

    *If of Irish descent - substitute, say, Welshman; if of Welsh ancestery - Scotsman; and so on!

At the outset of a 'fault-find', the sort of questions that should be asked are as follows:
(a) Where is the electrical system's wiring/circuit diagram? If it is not to hand, how is the circuit made up, of what does it consist - switches, fuses, lights, ignition switch...?
(b) Has the fault occurred previously.
(c) Are recent alterations, or repairs, causing the present problem?
(d) Could the breakdown simply be due to a blown fuse or tripped circuit breaker?

(e) Is the supposedly faulty equipment being operated correctly?

Once time has been taken to: think about the problem; consider the possible causes; and locate the wiring/circuit diagram - or at least find a sketch, or even an approximation, then fault-finding can commence - and let's hope there is still a fair distance to the lee shore!

It is as well to remember that a high percentage of electrical faults are due to bad connections, corrosion or poor installation - so first, closely inspect crimp, terminal and soldered joints. They are far more likely to be at fault than actual equipment failure.

The Basics

Whatever the fault, be it small or large, the ensuing basic procedures should be followed, one by one:-

(a) Operate the relevant keys, switches or buttons fitted in the defective item's circuit.
(b) Check the pertinent fuse/circuit breaker is not 'blown'.
(c) Using an electrical meter, or test lamp, measure the voltage at the nearest point to the defective unit, to which access can be easily gained. As long as + 12V (or + 24V) is apparent, then, unless the item requires a sensor or transducer to operate correctly (such as a depth sounder or oil pressure gauge), it must be defective, and should be repaired, or replaced.
(d) If no voltage is present at the point detailed in (b), then the wiring should be traced back to the next accessible point in the circuit, and another voltage measurement taken - a process repeated until a voltage of + 12V or (+ 24V) can be measured. Where this occurs, it is obvious that a fault exists between the places at which a voltage can, and cannot be measured. The item, or items, between those two locations must be defective, or have a bad connection, be it the wiring, a switch, or a fuse. It, or they, must be checked and replaced, if not repairable.

The preceding programme is a simple and effective, if theoretical method of fault-finding electrical circuits.

Oddly enough, one of the most difficult of the tasks is to locate convenient points at which to connect a meter, or test lamp, in order to take voltage measurements. It is also extremely important to be at ease and familiar with the operation of an electrical meter. It is easy to make simple mistakes by, for instance, selecting a wrong setting - which could result in a 'wild goose chase', thus confusing the situation even more. Unless conversant with the gear, consult the manufacturers' instructions, or read Chapter 4. And where is the shoreline now?

About 90% of the time a meter will be set to DC voltage, as by measuring voltages in a circuit, or circuits, tests can be made on all the wiring, switches, fuses (without even removing them!), and many other items.

A Simple Fault-find

Illustration 132 shows a simple circuit being investigated.

Illustration One Hundred & Thirty Two   Simple Circuit Checking

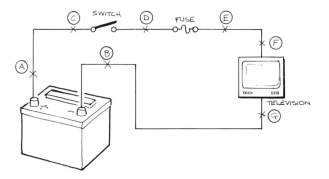

In this example, battery power is used to 'drive' a television. The crosses at (A) to (G) are accessible points on the circuit, where it should be possible to place a meter lead, in order to allow measurements to be taken. For example, points (A) and (B) are the battery terminals; points (C),

(D) and (E) are soldered (or crimp connections), to and from the switch and fuse, within the distribution panel; points (F) and (G) are the +ve and -ve terminals of a jack plug that connects into the +12V DC socket of the television set.

The scenario is that on arriving at the boat, on the Friday evening, the children, as usual, wish to watch even more television. The relevant distribution panel switch is turned on, followed by that on the television set... and nothing happens. What to do? That is, apart from attempting to telephone Rumblelows, and praying that the wretched thing will continue not to work! Well, obviously this calls for a visit to the pub. But seriously folks:-

(a) First locate the electrical meter and test it (as described in Chapter 4), ensuring 'meter confidence' and refreshing the 'little grey cells' in respect of its use!

(b) Then search out the wiring/circuit diagram of the boat (oh, ho, ho!) and, if available, soak up the details of the defective circuit.

(c) (Always) start at the faulty equipment (in this case the television) and locate the nearest connections, from which can be taken a voltage measurement, remembering that a +ve and -ve connection is required to make one. Referring to Illustration 132, these two points are (F) and (G). In this instance the television is fitted with a jack plug (Illustration 133), where point 'F' is the positive connection, and so should have the red meter lead connected to it, and point 'G' is the negative connection, to which should be affixed the black meter lead.

Illustration One Hundred & Thirty Three   A Jack Plug

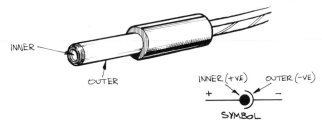

To take a meter measurement from a jack plug, place one of the meter leads on the outer terminal. For the other lead, open out, say, a paper clip and insert an end into the hole of the jack plug, so that it touches the inner terminal. Then the (other) test lead can be attached to the protruding wire (of the paper clip). The inner terminal is usually the positive one, although this is not always the case. The symbol for this type of plug is sketched and is sometimes displayed on equipment, adjacent to where the plug is located. If so, it indicates which is +ve and which is -ve.

(d) A jack plug is a common device for connecting the +ve and -ve of a DC supply to, for instance, televisions, radios, and calculators. It should be pulled out, a measurement taken, and if +12V (or +24V) is present, then the television is defective.

(e) If no voltage can be measured at the jack plug, then a break, or fault, must exist, somewhere in the circuit. To isolate this to a particular section of wire, a fuse, or piece of equipment, it is necessary to move one test lead at a time back to each accessible point in the circuit, taking a voltage measurement at each new point.
   In this example, and referring back to Illustration 132, the +ve (red) test lead should be moved from point (F) to point (E), and a second measurement taken. If +12V is recorded, then the fault is in the wire between point (E) and point (F). However, if again no voltage is measured, the +ve lead should be clipped on to the next contact, point (D), and a third reading taken. If this measures +12V, then the fuse, or its connections, must be faulty. If the measurement shows no voltage, then the process should be repeated at point (C) and, if necessary, point (A).

(g) Where a circuit has had to be traced, and 'metered', all the way back to the battery, with the +ve test lead, without being able to measure +12V, at any of the points, it is axiomatic that the fault lies in the negative supply circuit. This usually only consists of wiring, and possibly a few connections. The metering is repeated for the negative side of the circuit by moving the -ve (black) test lead back towards the battery, one point at a time, whilst keeping the +ve lead on the last point (A). If at any of the points +12V is measured, then it will be obvious that the fault lies between the point to which the -ve lead is attached and the previous one.

(h) The next point in the -ve circuit, after (G), is point (B), back at the battery. Unless the battery is flat or disconnected (in which case it would not only be the television on the 'blink'!), then +12V must be recorded between points (A) and (B). This means the fault must be in the wiring between point (G) and point (B) - but if all else fails, send the children home!

This example, although simplistic, outlines the basic concepts of fault-finding. The same method indicates the procedure to be followed to the majority of marine electrical faults, that is of starting at the defective item and working back towards the battery, one step at a time, remembering only to ever move one test lead at a time, taking a voltage measurement at each and every point, until +12V is measured.

Fault-finding Batteries & Alternators

When a fault occurs in a Battery or charging circuit (be it Alternator or Dynamo based), then possibly the first indication will be that the Battery struggles to 'power' the starter motor. Where a boat is fitted with an ammeter, or a battery charging lamp, then the malfunction should have become apparent earlier. For instance, if the battery charging lamp is lit when the engine is running, or the ammeter is not showing a positive current, then the Alternator/Dynamo is not correctly charging the Battery, for whatever reason.

Check List
The Battery

To investigate all faults in the charging circuit, follow the ensuing procedure:-

(a) Check the Battery condition, preferably with a hydrometer, but failing this with either a high rate discharge or normal electrical meter (*See* Chapter 5).

(b) If the Battery is in good condition and does not require replacing, measure its voltage as accurately as possible, making a note of the figure.

(c) Start the engine, setting the throttle to about ¼ maximum speed (with the gearbox in neutral), and remeasure the Battery voltage. If the charging circuit is working correctly, the readings should be approximately +12.5V for the Battery, without the engine running, and +13.2V or more, with the engine running.

Alternator/ Dynamo

(d) If the second battery reading is less than +13.2V, the Alternator/Dynamo might be defective, or the wiring to and from either could be faulty.

Where the system is fitted with an Alternator, carry out both the following two tests in order to check the wiring. If a Dynamo is the generator, only proceed with the first of the two.

(i) Check the wiring from the Alternator/Dynamo to the battery. To do so, ensure the engine is switched off, after which disconnect the +ve lead of the Alternator/Dynamo, and the +ve lead of the battery. Measure the resistance between the two disconnected leads (Illustration 134, Fig A). This should read less than 0.1 ohms.

If all is satisfactory, prior to reconnecting the two +ve leads, take a resistance measurement between the body of the the Alternator and the -ve of the battery. This also should measure less than 0.1 ohms.

(ii) Turn on the ignition switch, BUT DO NOT start the engine. Disconnect the field winding connection of the Alternator (Illustration 134, Fig B), and measure the voltage at this disconnected lead. It should read approximately the same as the battery voltage. If not, then the wiring between the battery, ignition switch, and the alternator must be checked, as well as the ignition switch.

If both the tests are satisfactory, the wiring is as it should be, and the Alternator/Dynamo must be defective.

(e) It should be noted that if + 12V is not connected, via the ignition switch, to the field winding connection of the alternator - then the alternator will not operate correctly, and thus not charge the battery. One cause of a 'lack of' + 12V supply is a broken ignition light bulb. Incidentally, the bulb should light up when the ignition is activated, and extinguish, once the alternator is supplying a higher voltage than the battery. The ignition light can be tested by disconnecting the alternator field winding connection, and shorting it to 0V (Illustration 134, Fig B) - when the bulb should illuminate.

Although a useful test, it is a repeat of that previously outlined (d ii), but following a slightly different procedure.

Illustration One Hundred & Thirty Four Metering an Alternator or Dynamo

Fig 134A Testing the Connection

DYNAMO
METER
BATTERY
METER
ALTERNATOR
BATTERY
ALTERNATOR
TO BATTERY WIRING

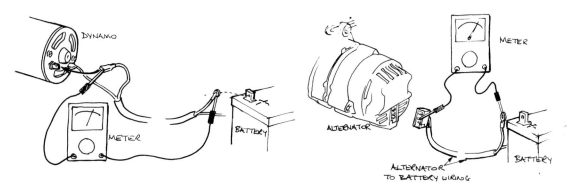

The meter reading should measure less than 0.1 ohms. If this is the case, then the wiring from the Alternator to the battery passes muster, and the generator is probably defective.

Fig 134B Metering the Generator

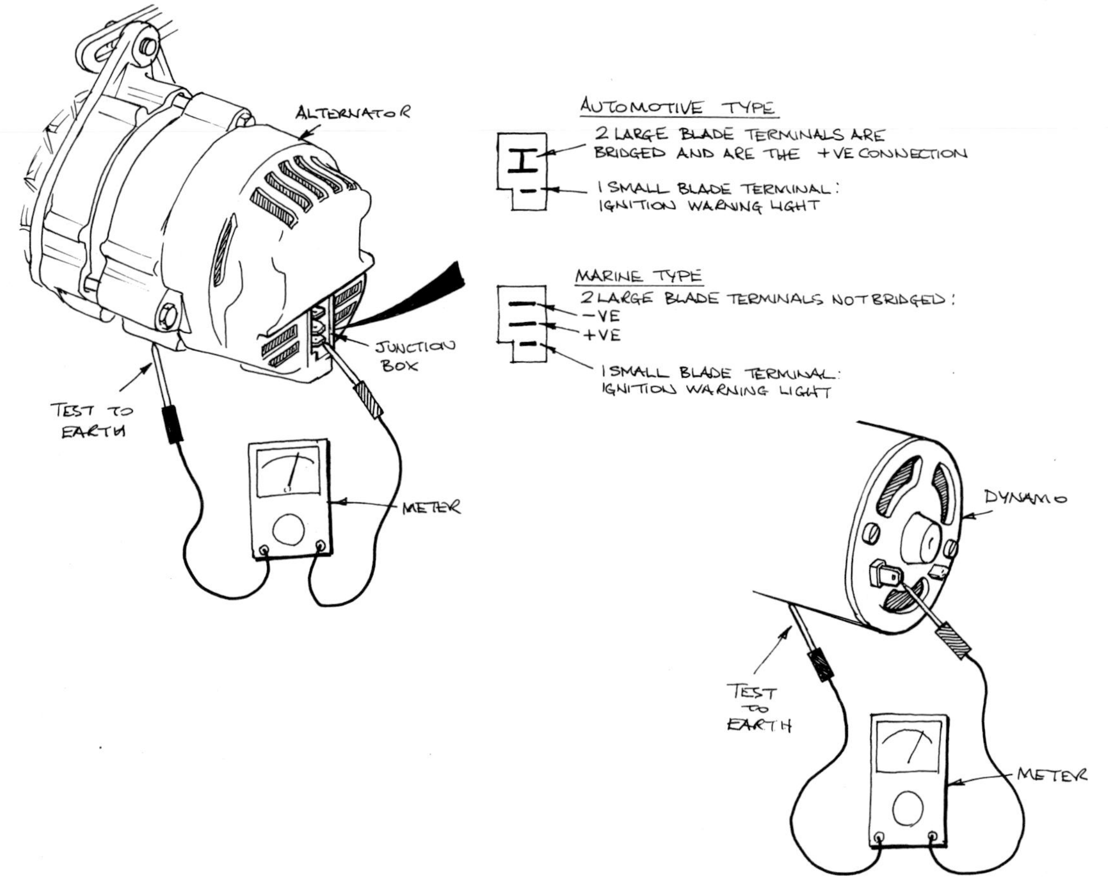

ALTERNATOR
AUTOMOTIVE TYPE
2 LARGE BLADE TERMINALS ARE
BRIDGED AND ARE THE +VE CONNECTION
1 SMALL BLADE TERMINAL:
IGNITION WARNING LIGHT
MARINE TYPE
2 LARGE BLADE TERMINALS NOT BRIDGED:
-VE
+VE
1 SMALL BLADE TERMINAL:
IGNITION WARNING LIGHT
JUNCTION
BOX
TEST TO
EARTH
METER
DYNAMO
TEST
TO
EARTH
METER

Note. If the ignition light bulb does not work - nor will the Alternator charge!'The why' is because the ignition wiring light is connected to the field windings.

Metering the Alternator field winding connection to 0V, despite values varying, should result in a reading of less than 100 ohms. It is not possible to meter the output of the stator windings of an Alternator due to the presence of the integral diodes.

It is possible to measure the resistance of a Dynamo's armature windings by metering between the +ve output terminal and 0V, usually the Dynamo body. This should be less than a few ohms.

When charging problems are experienced in a multiple battery system, employing blocking diodes or a split charge relay to isolate the craft's batteries, then the fault might originate in the aforementioned gadgetry.

Assuming that steps (a) to (c), of the previous example, have been made on all the batteries, and one or other are not receiving a charge, the fault may be due to:-

(a) Wiring/connection problems.
(b) A faulty Blocking Diodes/Split Charge Relay.

Testing Blocking Diodes & Split Charge Relay

To test Blocking Diodes (Illustration 135), proceed as follows.

Illustration One Hundred & Thirty Five   Blocking Diodes Circuitry

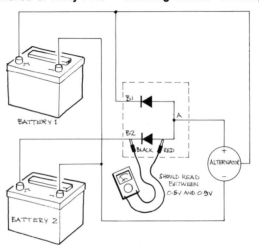

Blocking Diodes

(a) Turn the engine off and take a voltage measurement between the alternator connection to the Blocking Diodes and 0V, which should read 0V. If it does not, one or both of the Blocking Diodes has 'gone short'.

(b) Turn the engine on and place the red lead of the meter on the 'A' connection of the Blocking Diodes and the black lead on the 'B1' connection. This should result in a meter reading of between about 0.5V and 0.9V. Then move the black lead to the 'B2' connection, which ought to similarly 'meter'. If either reading is less than 0.5V, or more than 0.9V, or the first reading is not equal to approx 0V, then the Blocking Diodes are defective and must be replaced.

Split Charge Relay

To test a Split Charge Relay proceed as follows (Illustration 136).

Illustration One Hundred & Thirty Six   A Split Charge Relay Circuit

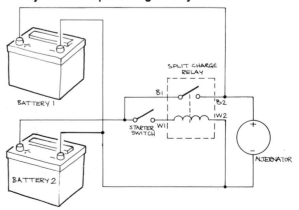

(a) Turn off the engine, after which remove the wire to the B1 connection. Measure the voltage between the B1 terminal and 0V. This should equal 0V.

(b) Now turn the engine on and repeat the previous measurement, as described in (a). This voltage should approximately equal the alternator charging voltage of 13.2V, or more. Record the exact reading. Then measure between the B2 terminal and 0V. There ought to be less than 0.1V difference between these two (B1 & B2) voltages. On the other hand, if there is not less than 0.1V difference, or the first reading was not equal to 0V, then the Split Charge Relay must be defective. As in the case of the blocking diodes, being a sealed unit, it cannot be repaired and should be replaced.

Starter Motors

An electrically faulty Starter Motor is a real problem these days, as fewer and fewer engines have 'handraulic' starting facilities. However, most Starter Motor defects are mechanical and may be caused by: a 'dirty' pinion; a worn or damaged commutator; or faulty brush gear (Illustration 137. Also *See* Chapter 6, and Illustrations 60, 61 & 62).

Illustration One Hundred & Thirty Seven   The Starter Motor

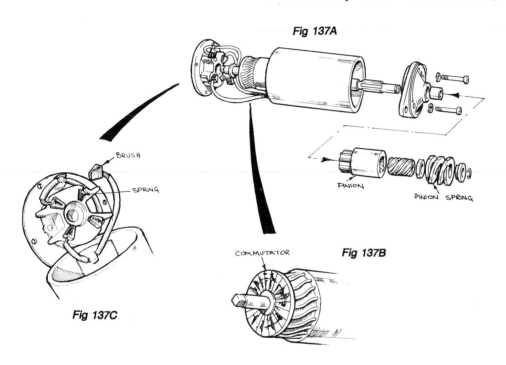

Fig 137A

Fig 137B

Fig 137C

BRUSH

SPRING

PINION

PINION SPRING

COMMUTATOR

Pinion

A dirty Starter Pinion causes sticking, resulting in either the Pinion not engaging, in which case the motor rotates and whirrs loudly, but does not turn the engine, or the Pinion stays engaged, after the starter key/switch has been released. This latter symptom must be cleared immediately, otherwise the Pinion may be irrevocably ruined. In either case, it is necessary to remove the starter motor to clean the Pinion, pinion spring and shaft (Illustration 137, Fig A), using petrol or methylated spirits (being careful not to let any fluid get inside the works). Do not oil the shaft, as this collects dirt, which may well cause a sticking Pinion!

Commutator

Should the Commutator be dirty, worn or damaged, then the appropriate action may include simply cleaning out the Commutator slots, having the Commutator re-machined or, in the case of severe damage, replacing the Commutator, and starter motor shaft (Illustration 137, Fig B).

Brush Gear

Damaged or worn Brush Gear may involve replacing the brushes, a broken brush spring or spring carrier (Illustration 137, Fig C).

Field Windings

Prior to moving on, test the Field Windings of the coils for a possible breakdown, although this is a very rare occurence (Illustration 138).

Illustration One Hundred & Thirty Eight   Starter Motor Windings

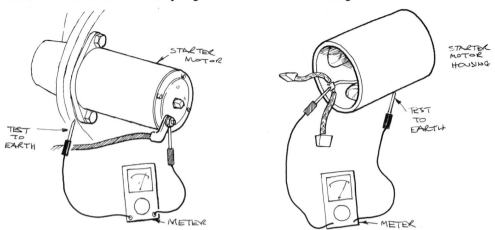

*Pre-engaged &
Inertia*

If the starter motor does not rotate at all, or only very slowly, then it is likely to be an electrical circuit fault. Illustration 139 (Figs A & B) details typical wiring for two of the most usual types of starter motors, Pre-engaged and Inertia. (Also *See* Chapter 6 & Illustration 63).

Illustration One Hundred & Thirty Nine   Starter Motor Wiring Circuits

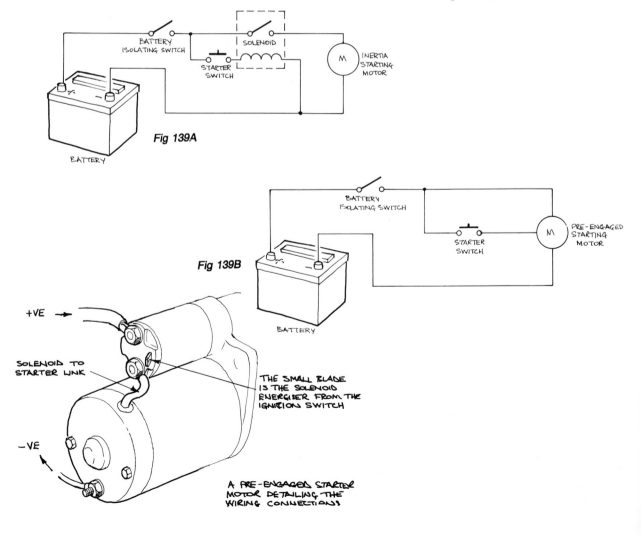

The following checks should be carried out to Starter Motor Wiring Circuits:-

(a) Measure the voltage across the battery terminals, as the starter switch is activated, ensuring that the engine will not actually start (for instance: shut off the fuel supply and open the decompression levers of a diesel engine; or remove the + 12V supply to the HT coil of a petrol engine).

   As soon as the starter motor engages, the battery voltage will drop considerably from its normal 12V (or more) reading. Keep the starter switch actioned for between 3 to 5 seconds, ensuring that the battery voltage stabilises, after the initial drop, to a value greater than 10V.

   If, whilst the starter motor is turning, the voltage reads less than 10V, then the battery is in need of charging/replacing.

(b) Assuming the battery proves to be satisfactory, then the wiring and components in the wiring circuit must be checked. This is to ensure there aren't any poor connections or high resistance, causing unwanted volt drops, thus restricting the power to the starter motor, causing it to turn slowly.

(c) To check the wiring, measure the voltage between the + ve battery terminal and the + ve connection of the starter motor, when the starter switch is operated. If a voltage of more than 1V is measured, a poor electrical connection or high resistance is present. If the voltage is less than 1V, repeat the test, this time measuring between the starter motor's -ve connection and the -ve terminal of the battery. This voltage should also be less than 1V, when the starter switch is in use. If not, a bad connection exists in the -ve wiring, between the starter motor and the battery. If either of the two measurements were greater than 1V, further measurements will have to be taken at other points in the starter motor to battery circuit, to deduce exactly which connection or component is faulty. This can often be done visually or by touching each connection, or item, to feel if it is hot. The latter 'warming' occurs when high currents are flowing, as they create heat as they pass through a resistance and or bad connection.

(d) If the battery is in 'apple pie order' and the circuit wiring, switches and solenoids satisfactory, then the starter motor itself is at fault, and should be replaced.

   When the starter switch is activated, and nothing happens, the following tests should be carried out:-

(a) Measure the voltage across the + ve and -ve poles of the battery. If the voltage is greater than 11.0V, then the battery is not at fault. If the reading is less, it will be unnecessary to look any further.

(b) Assuming the battery to be blameless, measure the voltage between the battery side of the battery Isolation Switch and the -ve battery connection (Illustration 140, Fig A). If the full battery voltage (+ 12V approx) is not measured, then that length of wiring, from the battery + ve connection to the switch, is poorly connected or broken. If approximately + 12V is measured, move the + ve test lead to the other, far side of the battery Isolation Switch (Illustration 140, Fig B). Should this not read approximately + 12V, the Isolation Switch is not correctly turned on, is defective or badly connected. *(See* Chapter 5, & Illustration 53).

Isolation Switch

(c) If the isolation switch is not at fault, the next item to test is the Ignition/Starter Switch (Illustration 140, Fig C). To carry this out, measure the voltage between the battery side of the Ignition/Starter Switch and the battery - ve connection. If there is + 12V (approx), the wiring to the starter switch passes muster. To continue, activate the switch and measure the voltage on the other far side of the switch. If this is approximately + 12V, then the switch must be satisfactory, if not, it must be replaced.

Ignition/Starter Switch

Illustration One Hundred & Forty   Meter Checks to Battery Isolator & Starter Switches

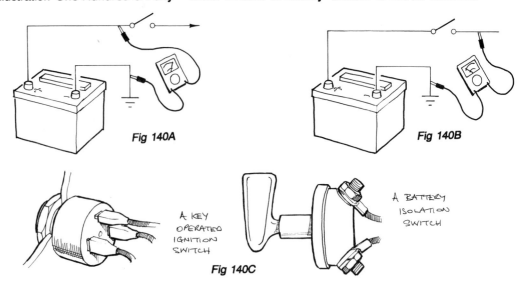

Fig 140A

Fig 140B

A KEY OPERATED IGNITION SWITCH

A BATTERY ISOLATION SWITCH

Fig 140C

Hot Wiring

Incidentally, to start an engine, in an emergency, it may have to be 'Hot Wired'. To initiate a 'Hot Wire', utilise a length of thick cable to make a short between the +ve battery connection and the +ve starter motor connection, and a thinner wire to connect the battery positive connection to the positive coil connection, having disconnected the starter switch (Illustration 141).

Illustration One Hundred & Forty One   'Hot Wire' Starting

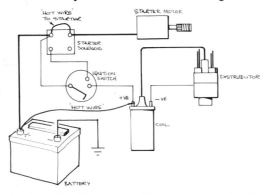

Solenoid

(d) If the starter motor is an inertia type, and it has a separate Solenoid, the latter can be checked. First measure the voltage across the two small connections of the Solenoid, as the starter switch is pressed (Illustration 142). These are a 0V and starter switch connection. If, when the starter switch is activated, approximately +12V is recorded, then the Solenoid is being energised correctly, and there will be a 'click' (from the Solenoid) as the starter switch is pressed. This is the noise of the Solenoid contacts closing together, as the Solenoid's coil is energised. If no click* is heard, the Solenoid is: very quiet, which is unlikely; the listener's hearing is not what it used to be; or, more likely, the Solenoid is defective.

* The click is not an entirely satisfactory 'health' check, as it can occur, even when the contacts are burnt - and won't 'drive' the starter.

(e) If it is certain that the Solenoid is being energised, next check that +12V (approx) is present at the starter motor's (large) connection from the isolation switch. If this is not the case, the wiring from the isolation switch to the Solenoid is likely to be defective/badly connected (or the Solenoid contacts are burnt out).

Illustration One Hundred & Forty Two A Starter Solenoid & Electrical Connections

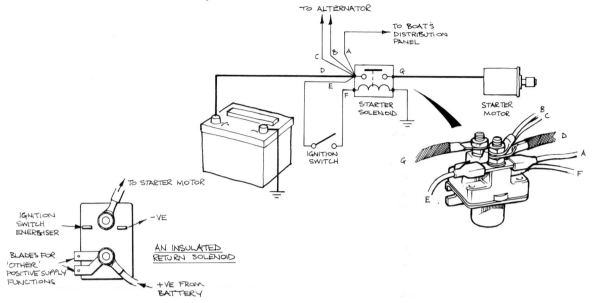

Readers should note that the Starter Solenoid is a very convenient point/connection from which to 'extract' a 12V supply - thus there may be a number of other wires, 'coming and going'.

(f) To check that the Solenoid is switching correctly, which it may not be doing, even if it does 'click', disconnect the (thick) cable to the starter motor from the Solenoid, and take a resistance measurement across the two large connections of the Solenoid. When the starter switch is not pressed the resistance should be very high (>1M ohms, or one million ohms), but as soon as the switch is pressed, the resistance should drop to less than 0.1 ohms. Should this not be so, then the Solenoid is in need of replacement.

(g) If the Solenoid is working correctly, re-connect the lead to it, measure the voltage between the two connections to the starter motor. When the starter switch is pressed, this should be +12V (approx). If it is not, there must be a faulty/bad connection in the wiring between the Solenoid and the starter motor, or between the -ve terminal of the battery and the starter motor. If +12V (approx) is measured, the starter motor must be defective and should be replaced.

If a Petrol Engine installation will not start, it is very likely that the reason lies within the electrical Ignition System. This can be broken down into two distinct sections, referred to as the Low Tension and High Tension circuits (Illustration 143).

A Petrol Engine Ignition System

Illustration One Hundred & Forty Three A Petrol Engine Ignition System

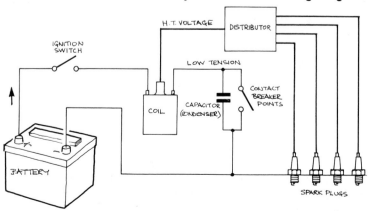

Low Tension
Circuit

The Low Tension Circuit consists of all the +12V items, namely the battery, contact breaker points, condenser, ignition switch, and the primary winding of the coil.

High Tension
Circuit

The High Tension (HT) Circuit carries the very high voltages (5000V or more) and consists of the distributor, sparking plugs and the secondary winding of the coil.

(Back to the)
Low Tension

When a fault occurs in the ignition system, it is best to start investigations 'in amongst' the Low Tension side of things - it is the easiest to check! To carry this out, the following procedures should be followed:-

Ignition Switch

(a) As the Ignition Switch is often difficult to access, it is probably worth first measuring that +12V is getting to the coil. If this proves not to be the case, it will be necessary to check the Ignition Switch and associated wiring. Place the black test lead on a convenient 0V connection (such as the engine block), and the red lead on the +ve coil connection from the Ignition Switch. If +12V (approx) is measured, when the Ignition Switch is turned on, the wiring from the battery to the ignition switch, the Ignition Switch itself, and the wiring from it to the coil, pass the test.

(b) Next, move the red lead to the -ve coil connection of the coil and measure the voltage. This will be either +12V (approx.), or 0V, depending at which position the contact breaker points have come to rest. If the engine is turned over, using a spanner on the crankshaft pulley nut, it should be possible to see the voltage switching between 0V and +12V (approx), as the contact breaker points open and close. If this is the case, then the low tension circuit is functioning correctly.
NB The above only checks that the components and wiring are electrically functional, it does not indicate that, for instance, the timing of the ignition system is correct.

(c) If the voltage is not switching between 0V and +12V (approx), a fault must exist in the contact breaker points, the capacitor/condenser, or the wiring between the coil and contact breaker points.

The Distributor

To find out which is at fault, remove The Distributor cap and rotor arm to reveal the contact breaker points (Illustration 144), that is unless the unit is fitted with electronic, 'pointless', or solid state ignition. If this is the case it will be necessary to employ an engineer with the necessary, specialised equipment and test gear, as these systems are beyond the ability of most DIY electricians.

Illustration One Hundred & Forty Four   The Distributor

Fig 144A

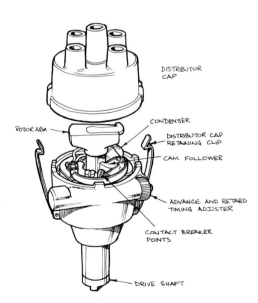

DISTRIBUTOR CAP

CONDENSER

ROTOR ARM

DISTRIBUTOR CAP RETAINING CLIP

CAM FOLLOWER

ADVANCE AND RETARD TIMING ADJUSTER

CONTACT BREAKER POINTS

DRIVE SHAFT

Contact
Breaker
Points

(d) Assuming that the engine possesses 'good', old-fashioned points, continue to turn the engine over until they open. Incidentally, if they do not open, 'kick thyself', as this may be the fault, and the Contact Breaker points simply require resetting. Check that the contact faces are in good condition, replacing them if not. As a first aid measure, dress badly pitted contacts with a special file or, if really desperate, use an emery board placed between them, and gently moved fore and aft, to ensure the surfaces are square. Consequently 'gap' the points (Illustration 144 Fig B).

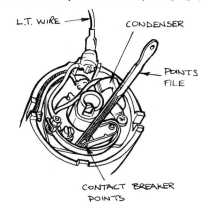

Fig 144B

(e) If the Contact Breaker points are opening and closing satisfactorily, turn the engine over until the points are open. Place the red test lead on first one, and then the other of the contacts - approximately +12V should be measured, on one of them. If not, then the wiring or connections between the coil and the points must be defective.

   If +12V (approx) is recorded at both of the contacts, check that the condenser has not 'gone short', by disconnecting one of its connections and measuring the voltage on the two contacts again. If only one of them now measures +12V (approx), the condenser is defective and must be replaced. If both are still measuring +12V, a short or poor connection must exist somewhere in and or around the distributor, which should show up with a thorough visual check. A particular item to inspect, is the low tension connection which leads in the side of the distributor body, to wire up to the points and the condenser. Incidentally, if the Contact Breaker points do not last very long before becoming charred or pitted, the condenser is likely to be defective and should be changed.

Once satisfied with 'matters' low tension, check the High Tension (HT) Circuit. This can only be carried out visually by inspecting:-

(Back to the) High Tension Circuit

(a) That all the HT leads are firmly screwed/pushed in to the: tops of the sparking plugs, and the coil; recesses of the distributor cap; and, should suppressors be fitted, in the HT leads, that they are firmly screwed into the lead ends (See Illustration 76).
(b) That none of the HT leads have broken, cracked or cut insulation.
(c) That the distributor cap is not chipped, deeply scored or cracked; and that the internal contacts of the distributor cap are not charred, pitted or worn.
(d) That the rotor arm is not badly cracked, charred, pitted or worn.
(e) That the sparking plugs are in good condition, and set to the recommended gap.

Incidentally, one highly effective method of looking for HT faults is to observe the set-up in darkness, with the engine running. In these circumstances, any tracking, short-cuts or 'misbehaviour' of the high-tension spark can be easily seen. Should there be doubt about any of the aforementioned items, replace them.

(f) If both the low and high tension circuits have checked out, and appear to be in working order, there is a possibility that the Ignition Coil is defective. That is to say, it is not correctly converting the low voltage pulse (+12V) into a high voltage spark (5000V or more).

Ignition Coil

   The Ignition Coil (See Chapter 6 & Illustration 74) actually consists of two coils, referred to as the primary and secondary windings. It is very important that both have the correct number of turns of wire, as the ratio of turns of wire on each winding directly effects the size of voltage of the HT spark. Sometimes these windings burn out or break down and cause weak HT sparks to be generated. To check a Coil it is necessary to measure the resistance of each winding with a meter (Illustration 145). If either of these resistances are incorrect, then the Ignition Coil is defective and should be replaced, as these units are irreparable.

Illustration One Hundred & Forty Five   The Coil

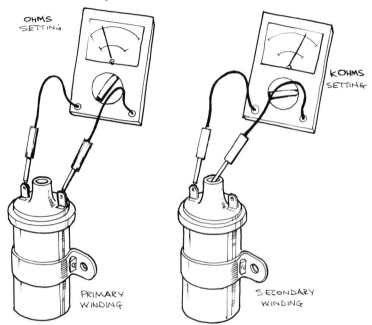

First disconnect all the wires to the Coil, after which measure the resistance of the primary (Low Tension) windings first. Set the meter to the lowest resistance range and place one lead each on the two Low Tension connections. This should measure between about 0.5 ohms and 1 ohms, for most Ignition Coils.

The secondary (High Tension) windings can be measured by placing one lead on the HT connection, and the other lead on either of the two Low Tension connections. The secondary coil should measure between 4000 ohms and 10000 ohms (4 to 10k ohms).

Electronic Instruments

When Electronic Instruments fail to work, there is little that can be done if they are defective. However, most faults are due to poor connections or transducer failure.

The first and most important check on all electronic equipment is that the +12V (or 24V) supply voltage is correct. Using a meter, measure the voltage to the rear of the Instrument. Unfortunately, quite often this will be impossible, because of the lack of connections, as the wiring comes directly out of the unit, or due to special connections, to which meter probes cannot be placed. Where this is the case, then the Instrument's wires must be traced back to the very first connections, where a measurement can be taken. If a supply voltage of 10.5V, or more, is present, then a fault must exist in the Instrument.

It must be borne in mind that much electronic equipment cannot work correctly with a supply voltage of 10V, or less. If the full +12V is not being supplied, this could well be the reason for the poor performance, or non-operation of, say, a depth sounder.

Depth Sounders

The following describes various checks to make to different types of Instruments:-
(a) Depth Sounders have a minimum of four connections, two for the +12V supply to the instrument, and two for the transducer, or thru' hull sender unit. Any extra connections are not likely to be critical to the operation of the unit and are, typically, outputs to drive a repeater unit, or any other piece of equipment that accepts depth information. In most cases, it is likely to be the instrument at fault, as there is more to go wrong in their 'insides'.
  (i) Check the wiring to the transducer and that the connections to the Depth Sounder are satisfactory, and not loose or corroded.

(ii) Confirm there are no signs of physical damage that may have resulted from an object falling against the wiring.

Should the above not reveal any defects, then it is difficult to do more. Neither Depth Sounder transducers, nor PCB's (Printed Circuit Boards) for that matter, can be tested without specialist gear and knowledge. It is a lot easier to remove the instrument and send it back to the manufacturer, than to remove a boat from the water, in order to remove the transducer - only to discover it is not faulty.

(b) Logs are similar to depth sounders, having a minimum of four connections - two for the power and two for the transducer, or thru' hull sender unit. Further connections are likely to be outputs for repeaters, or other instruments. However, more modern Logs, offering other features, such as wind speed, engine hours, and sea temperature, may have considerably more than four connections. If so, consult the installation/instruction manual for details.

Logs

(i) First inspect the transducer. Some of the more expensive Logs employ ultrasonic units and require specialist test gear, thus only the wiring can be visually checked. However, if the Log uses a trailing or paddle-wheel transducer it is no problem to inspect.

(ii) With a Trailing Transducer, set the electric meter to DC volts, and measure the voltage across the two Transducer connections, whilst it is slowly rotated by hand. The voltage should be observed switching between +12V and 0V, and then back again, once or twice every revolution. (*Note*: it may be between +5V and 0V, depending on the make of log). If this happens, and the Transducer spins smoothly, without too much effort, everything is in order.

Trailing Transducer

(iii) A Paddle-wheel Transducer should be removed from the thru' hull skin fitting, (*See* Illustration 119), remembering to replace it with the blanking plug, quickly! Give it a visual check, ensuring that it spins freely and that no sea-life has made its home in the space around the paddle-wheel. Next count the number of wires from the paddle-wheel to the instrument head. If there are two, then the Transducer either has a magnet and reed switch, in which case it can be tested as set out in the description for the trailing log, or it is a magnet and coil type unit. To inspect the latter, set the meter to AC volts and measure the voltage between the two Transducer connections to the instrument. As the paddle-wheel is spun, a small AC voltage should be observed, the size of which varies, depending on the particular manufacturer of the unit. Initially, set the meter to the smallest AC voltage range, increasing if necessary. The faster the paddle-wheel is spun, the larger the voltage. This is because the more swiftly the magnet passes the coil, the more energy (voltage) will be induced in the coil - and not because there are more pulses. A typical reading should be about 0.1V AC.

Paddle-wheel Transducer

If the Paddle-wheel has three wires, between it and the instrument head, then it is a 'Hall Effect' switch type Transducer. To investigate, set the meter to DC volts, and refer to the instrument's instruction manual to confirm the function of each of the wires. Two of them will be the +12V and 0V supply lines, required because the 'Hall Effect' switch requires a +12V supply to operate. The third cable will be the signal wire, that carries the pulses from the Transducer to the instrument head, where they are counted. First verify that the two wires supplying +12V to the Transducer, do in fact have +12V across them. If not, then the instrument head is defective. Assuming there is +12V, connect the meter across the signal wire and the 0V wire. Whilst slowly turning the Transducer Paddle-wheel, each revolution should result in the meter switching between +12V and 0V, at least once, possibly twice, depending on the make and model of Transducer. If no switching is observed, the Transducer is defective and should be changed. (*Note*: some log Transducers switch between +5V and 0V, rather than +12V and 0V, so there is no need to panic if only +5V is measured. If in doubt, consult with the manufacturer).

Wind Instruments have a minimum of six connections, two providing power to the instrument and four, or more, wires connect the masthead unit, or transducer, to the instrument (*See* Illustration 123).

Wind Instruments

(1) First check the circuits, wires, fuses and connections. If + 12V is available at the instrument's power connections, check the transducer connections. By referring to the instruction manual, work out which carry the + 12V supply to the transducer, which carry the wind speed pulses to the instrument, and which wire/wires transmit the wind angle signals to the Instrument.

(2) Ensure that + 12V and 0V are available at the transducer, by measuring with a meter set to DC volts. This + 12V supply is often fused in the Instrument, or its control/ connection box. If + 12V is not available, inspect the fuse.

(3) If + 12V is present at the transducer, ensure the wind speed signal is pulsing, by connecting a meter across the wind speed signal wire and 0V. The voltage should be seen to be switching between + 12V and 0V, in the same manner as the 'Hall Effect' type log paddle-wheel signal. If it does not, then the transducer is defective.

(4) Next check the wind angle signal, or signals, which come in three basic types:-
  (i) Single-phase: They consist of a variable resistor, that rotates as the wind direction changes, and whose resistance changes accordingly. They do not give the full 360° of wind direction, only providing about 305°. There is solely one wire to provide a signal back to the Instrument. The voltage varies between 30° and 330° linearly (Illustration 146, Fig A). By placing a meter on the signal wire and the 0V wire, the voltage should vary as the wind angle vane rotates through 360°. If this occurs, then the transducer is working correctly.

Illustration One Hundred & Forty Six   Wind Instrument Phasing

Fig 146A   Single-phase

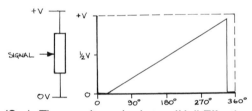

  (ii) Double-phase (Sin/Cos): These units embody two 'Hall Effect' sensors, similar to 'Hall Effect' switches, or two inductive sensors. The sensors detect which direction the wind vane is pointing, and hence the direction the wind is blowing. This is usually achieved by having a permanent magnet attached to the wind vane, the sensors detecting the direction of the north and south poles of the magnet, and thus the wind direction. The voltage relationship of the sensors to wind direction is usually 'pseudo sinusoidal' (Yes!). As one of them is positioned at 90° to the other, the resulting two waveforms, produced by the pair, have a sine and cosine relationship (Illustration 146, Fig B). The Wind Instrument can then monitor these two signals and work out the sine and cosine values. From these can be calculated the wind angle.

Fig 146B   Double-phase

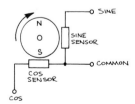

If a double-phase wind transducer is involved, it is worth contacting the manufacturer of the equipment, to find out what voltages the transducer produces, for various angles, before fault-finding the system. It must be noted that an expert is, more often than not required to repair this type of transducer.

(iii) Three-phase: This type of instrument consists of a special, variable resistor that has three connections, instead of the one of a single-phase device. As the wind angle alters, so the pot rotates and the voltage on each of the three connections changes (Illustration 146, Fig C).

Fig 146C   Three-phase

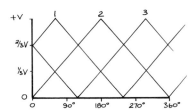

The three wires must be checked, by placing the meter across whichever connection is to be measured and 0V. The voltage should go up and down during one revolution of the wind vane. If each phase appears to be in order, the wind angle transducer is working correctly.

Positional Systems & Radio

Positional or Radio Navigational Systems and Radios all consist of a radio receiver and an aerial/antenna. They include:- Global Positioning (GPS); Loran; Decca; VHF Radio; and AM/FM Radios. 'Day to day' fault-finding is limited to checking that 12V is 'getting' to the instrument and that all the cables are connected correctly. The aerial/antenna cannot be electrically checked, other than by an experienced engineer, with the relevant test equipment. If, however, the aerial is mounted at the top of a mast, it may well have a thru' deck connector and this should be inspected, to ensure it is not corroded or dirty and causing a poor junction.

GPS, Loran and Decca systems are all susceptible to electrical noise, and if an instrument is not giving a satisfactory positional fix, it is worth checking the 'signal to noise' ratio. This is usually capable of being displayed, for details of which, refer to the relevant instruction manual.

Autopilots

Autopilots can only be investigated, by the DIY handyman, to ensure that +12V is available at the equipment, and that all the connections are satisfactory.

Mains Supply Circuits

Where a boat is fitted with a Mains Supply Circuit, for use when moored, or with an inverter, or generator to 'feed' a 240V circuit, then proceed as follows:-
(a) Either disconnect the plug from the shore supply, or turn off the generator/engine, if the source of 240V AC supply is located aboard the boat. This is mandatory, repeat mandatory, as no mains voltages must be present in any circuitry to be checked. If in doubt, double check, and then once again - it could save one's life.
(b) Testing for Continuity. Deploying an electrical meter, measure the resistance between the live connection of the disconnected plug, or generator, and the live of each of the boat's sockets (Illustration 147).

Continuity

Illustration One Hundred & Forty Seven   Metering the Mains

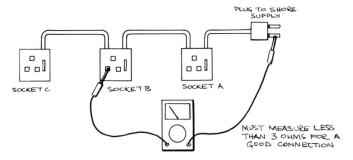

Due to the distance between the supply plug/generator and the sockets, it may be necessary to use a spare piece of 'known', good condition wire as a test extension lead.

If the resistance of the plug, or generator's live connection to any of the socket's live connections, is greater than about 3 ohms, there is a fault.

Carry out the same series of measurements for the neutral connections of the plug/generator and each of the sockets.

(c) The earth connection of a mains system does not directly effect the operation of the installation, for if it was disconnected equipment would still work. But, as long as it is wired correctly, the earth provides a safety device against equipment casings and bodies becoming live - and electrocuting the user. For this reason, if no other, the earth must be checked, in the same manner as the live and neutral connections.

(d) Should any of the measurements be greater than 3 ohms, there must be a wiring fault. The most likely cause 'lies' in the connections to the particular socket measuring a high resistance.

Referring back to Illustration 147, if the live connection of socket B measured infinite resistance ('open circuit') to the live connection of the shore supply plug, there is a fault. If the resistance between socket A and the shore supply plug was acceptable (less than 3 ohms), the fault must lie in the connection to socket B, the wire from socket A to socket B, or the connection of this wire to socket A.

The connections to and from sockets A and B can be checked by unscrewing the sockets and visually inspecting the wiring, or gently pulling each wire, to see if one is loose. If these prove to be satisfactory, there could be a fault in the wire itself, but this is the least likely explanation, so always inspect connections first.

Shorts

(e) Testing for Short-circuits (Shorts). If the circuit breakers, or fuses, for the mains supply continues to trip out, or blow, there is a good chance that an intermittent or constant fault has occurred in the wiring.

Tracing a Short can prove extremely time-consuming, so much so that it may be well worth pursuing the matter 'mechanically'. That is by unscrewing all the sockets and inspecting each and every connection, searching for loose wires that have touched other wires, or small metal objects that have bridged the gap between two connections. If this does not locate the fault, then it is a case of starting at the shore supply plug (Illustration 148) and measuring the resistance of:-

(i)   The live connection to the neutral.

(ii) The live connection to the earth.

(iii) The neutral connection to the earth.

The resistance of each of the above should be greater than 1M ohms (1,000,000 ohms). Where this is not the case, then those are the 'Shorted' connections. Once the Short-circuit has been located, it is mandatory to work through the circuit, socket by socket, measuring the resistance of the two 'Shorted' connections at each. However, it is necessary, at every socket, to disconnect the wires from the last item checked.

Illustration One Hundred & Forty Eight   Locating A 'Short'

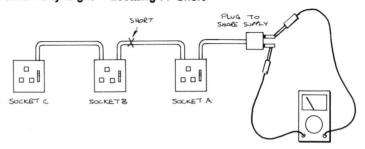

(f) For instance, referring to illustration 148, it will be noted that the cable from socket A to socket B has a 'Short', maybe due to a heavy or sharp object being placed on or against the cable, causing two of the three wires, within, to Short-circuit. For the sake of this example, let us assume that it is the live and neutral wires that are 'Shorting'.

Initially, move to the first item in the circuit - socket A. Here the cable from the shore plug is disconnected, isolating the shore plug and its length of cable from the rest of the circuit. Then a measurement is taken of the resistance of the two 'Shorted' connections - live and neutral, at socket A. If this were to show a resistance greater than 1M ohms (i.e. no 'Short'), the rest of the circuit is alright and the shore plug, or its length of cable, is at fault.

In this example though, a 'Short' would continue to show up between the live and neutral at socket A, as the fault is further on in the circuit. The next step is to move to socket B and disconnect the cable from socket A, thus isolating socket A and its cable from the rest of the circuit. A measurement of the resistance between live and neutral is taken at socket B. As the cable from socket A to socket B has been disconnected, the resistance measurement will be greater than 1M ohms, indicating that the rest of the circuit is satisfactory.

Therefore, Dr Watson, the 'Short' must be in the last items to be disconnected, that is socket A and (its) cable. Once located, socket A and its cable can be repaired, or replaced, and the fault cleared. Before the circuit can be used again, all the items that were disconnected, prior to the fault being found, will have to be re-connected.

NOTE: Where mains wiring is disconnected for any reason, and then re-connected, it is very important that the wiring is given one last test for Continuity and 'Shorts', as previously detailed, before re-applying mains voltages.

CHAPTER TWELVE

ABBREVIATIONS, SYMBOLS, GLOSSARY, EQUATIONS & FORMULAE, TABLES AND USEFUL NAMES & ADDRESSES

ABBREVIATIONS/SYMBOLS

A	Amps or ampere - a unit of current flow
AC	Alternating current
AF	Audio frequency
AGC	Automatic gain control
Ah	Ampere-hour
AM	Amplitude Modulation
AVO	Amps-volts-ohms meter
cm	Centimetre
C	Centigrade
CR	Symbol for capacitor-resistor circuit
CSA	Cross-sectional area
DC	Direct current
Dia	Diameter
DMM	Digital multi-meter
DPDT	Double Pole Double Throw
DPST	Double Pole Single Throw
DVM	Digital voltmeter
ELB	Earth leakage breaker
EMF	Electro motive force, or voltage
F	Farad
FM	Frequency modulation
GFI	Ground fault interrupter
GPS	Global positioning system

H	Henry
HP	Horsepower
HT	High Tension
Hz	Hertz
I	Current, in a formula
kHz	Kilohertz
kg	Kilogramme
kW	Kilowatt
kWh	Kilowatt-hour
L	Symbol for inductance
LC	Symbol for an inductor-capacitor circuit
LCD	Liquid crystal display
LED	Light emitting diode
m	Metre
mF	Millifarad
MHz	Megahertz
mm	Millimetre
MW	Megawatt
mW	Milliwatt
O	Ohms
OD	Outside diameter
OTT	'Over The Top'
PCB	Printed circuit board
POT	Potentiometer
PTFE	Poly Tetra Fluoro Ethylene
PVC	Polyvinyl chloride
R	Abbreviation for resistance
RF	Radio frequency
RFI	Radio frequency interference
RPM	Revs per minute
RT or R/T	Radio telephone
SB	Sidebands (radio)
SNR	Signal to noise ratio
SPDT	Single pole double throw
SPST	Single pole single throw
SSB	Single sideband (radio)
SWG	Standard wire gauge
uF	Microfarad
uH	Micro-Henry
UHF	Ultra high frequency
V	Volt
VHF	Very high frequency
VOM	Volt-ohm meter
W	Watt - The unit of electrical power
X	Reactance
Z	Impedance

CIRCUIT DIAGRAM SYMBOLS

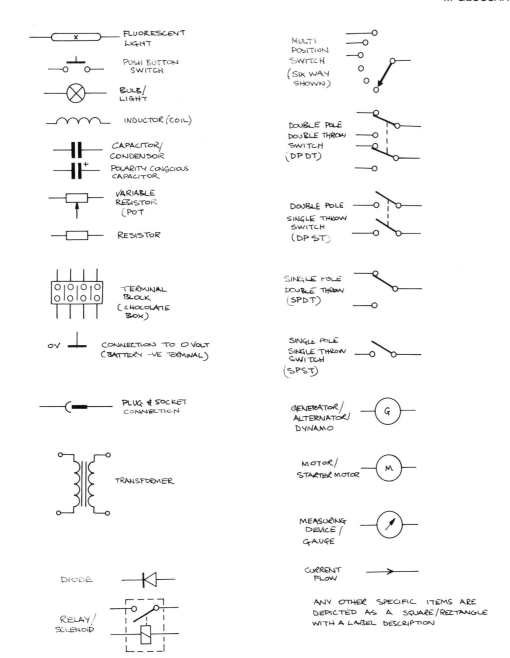

FLUORESCENT LIGHT

PUSH BUTTON SWITCH

BULB/ LIGHT

INDUCTOR (COIL)

CAPACITOR/ CONDENSOR

POLARITY CONGCIOUS CAPACITOR

VARIABLE RESISTOR (POT

RESISTOR

TERMINAL BLOCK (CHOCOLATE BOX)

0V   CONNECTION TO 0 VOLT (BATTERY -VE TERMINAL)

PLUG & SOCKET CONNECTION

TRANSFORMER

DIODE

RELAY/ SOLENOID

MULTI POSITION SWITCH (SIX WAY SHOWN)

DOUBLE POLE DOUBLE THROW SWITCH (DPDT)

DOUBLE POLE SINGLE THROW SWITCH (DPST)

SINGLE POLE DOUBLE THROW (SPDT)

SINGLE POLE SINGLE THROW SWITCH (SPST)

GENERATOR/ ALTERNATOR/ DYNAMO   G

MOTOR/ STARTER MOTOR   M

MEASURING DEVICE/ GAUGE

CURRENT FLOW

ANY OTHER SPECIFIC ITEMS ARE DEPICTED AS A SQUARE/RECTANGLE WITH A LABEL DESCRIPTION

GLOSSARY

A

Aerial - conductor for radiating, or receiving radio signals.

Alligator Clip - a spring-loaded metal clip with serrated jaws.

Alkaline - the electrolyte in Nickel-cadmium batteries.

Alternating Current (AC) - an electrical current, reversing its direction at regular intervals. Each repetition of a change is a cycle, and the number of cycles taking place, in one second, is the frequency.

Alternator - a machine for generating electricity by spinning a magnet inside a series of coils. The resulting power output is alternating current. For DC systems, this output is rectified via diodes.

Ammeter - an instrument for measuring current flow, in amperes.

Ampere (amp) - a measure of the rate of electric current flow.

Ampere-hour (Ah) - The term defining the storage capability of batteries. The quoted figure normally applies at a 10 hour rate, thus, an 80 Ah battery could supply an 8A discharge, for 10 hours.

Amplification - The magnification achieved, between the input and output terminations, from a mechanical or electrical device.

Amplifier - a circuit for increasing the strength of voltage, or current.

Amplitude Modulation (AM) A means of applying intelligence to an electrical signal, by varying its instantaneous amplitude.

Analogue - electronic circuitry which has linear operating conditions producing an output signal directly analogous to its input.

Anode - the positive terminal of a battery, or cell.

Anodic protection - the fitting of sacrificial pieces of metal (more often than not zinc or magnesium), usually below the water-line, in order to protect other metals from galvanic/electrolytic corrosion.

Antenna - *See* Aerial

Arcing - The generation of 'stray', unwanted electrical sparks that occur when a current flows between two electrodes, separated by a gap, and usually the result of 'poor', inefficient contacts.

Armature - the rotating windings in a generator (AC or DC).

Attenuate - to decrease the strength.

Atom - the smallest part of an element that retains its chemical identity and can take part in a chemical reaction.

Autopilot - a power-driven device for steering a boat on a preset compass course.

Auxiliary coil - an additional set of windings, in the stator of some AC alternators, used to power a voltage regulator, or battery charging circuit.

AVO meter - *See* Multi-meter

B

Background Noise - Natural, or man-made electrical interference.

Band Width - the range of frequencies above and below the frequency required for receiving a particular transmitted signal.

Battery (marine or automotive) - A collection of cells, with a liquid electrolyte, usually connected in series, to provide a source of electrical power. NB This description does not apply to dry cell batteries, such as those fitted to torches. *See* Cell.

Battery capacity - *See* Ampere-hours

Battery isolation switch - a switch, installed close to the battery, to completely isolate the battery.

Battery sensed - a voltage regulator, sensing system voltage at the battery - as opposed to at the alternator.

Beacon - a transmitting station used for navigational purposes.

Blocking Diodes - special diodes fitted into multiple battery installations, to 'automatically' isolate the batteries from each other, when not being charged by a generator. *See* Diode.

Bonding - the process of electrically linking all items of equipment, to create a common potential, usually for the purpose of cathodic protection, or suppression of interference.

Bridge rectifier - an arrangement of diodes for converting alternating current (AC) to direct current (DC). *See* Rectifier.

Brush - a carbon, or carbon composite bar, usually spring-loaded, used to conduct current to or from commutators, or slip rings, of generators and starter motors.

Bypass - a capacitor providing a 'detour' for alternating currents.

C

Cable clamp - a U-shaped bracket used to fix wiring and cable-runs to a batten or bulkhead, or to provide strain relief for wiring.

Cable tie - *See* Cable clamp

Capacitor - a device for storing electric energy. A capacitor allows alternating current (AC) to pass, but blocks the flow of direct current (DC). The unit indicating the quantity of charge a specific capacitor can store is the Farad or, more commonly, the microfarad (uF).

Cathode - the negative terminal of a battery or cell.

Cell - a single unit, that 'generates' and stores electricity through chemical energy, a number of which are grouped together to form a battery.

Charge - an excess, or deficiency, of electrons in a material

Choke - an inductance, or coil, used to impede alternating current (AC), and designed to filter out unwanted radio noise.

Circuit - the path of electric current.

Circuit breaker - a current sensitive switch, which trips open if the designed ratings are exceeded.

Coaxial cable - a specially constructed cable designed for the transmission of high frequency AC signals.

Commutator - the copper segments arranged around one end of an armature and from which brushes collect the generated current.

Condenser - a capacitor.

Conductance - a measure of a material's ability to conduct electricity.

Conductor - any material through which electric current can easily flow

Conduit - a protective pipe, or trunking, in which electric cables are routed.

Convertor - a device changing one form of energy, or signal, to another. Also known as an Inverter. Examples are power convertors used to convert, say, a boat's 12V supply to 240V AC 50 Hz, to 'drive' mains equipment.

Corrosion - a process of wasting that leads to the destruction of two or more metals.

Crimp terminal - a terminal end fitting squeezed on to electric cables, with a special tool.

Current - the rate of flow of electricity, measured in amps.

Cycle - a complete move - from zero to positive, to zero to negative, and back to zero. *See* Alternating current.

D

Deep cycle battery - a specially constructed battery designed to withstand prolonged, heavy discharges, without suffering internal damage.

Diffusion - the process by which the acid in a battery electrolyte permeates the active material of the cell plates.

Digital - circuitry which performs its specific function by using pulses or 'digits' of various rates or lengths, and constant amplitude.

Diode - an electronically 'non-value' valve. A diode consists of two pieces of semi-conductor material, one piece + ve, and the other piece -ve, that only allow current to flow through them, in one direction.

Dipole - an aerial with two elements, usually employed at VHF for marine purposes.

Direct current (DC) - an electric current, that flows in one direction only.

Double pole switch (DPS) - a switch that makes or breaks two separate connections, at the same time.

Drip loop - a deliberately formed, downward loop placed in a run of electrical wire, to keep moisture out of terminal boxes, and junctions.

Duplexer - a device to allow a transmitter and receiver to be used simultaneously from a common aerial.

Dynamo - *See* Generator

E

Earth - the reference point ('ground potential') for AC circuits.

Earth leak - a current leak to earth, or ground, but via the wiring circuit.

Electric motor - a device for converting electric power into rotary mechanical motion. *See* Induction motors.

Electrolysis - *See* Corrosion.

Electrolyte - a solution capable of carrying electric current.

Electrolytic corrosion - corrosion arising as a result of electrolysis. *See* Galvanic corrosion.

Electro-magnet - a magnet, the magnetic field of which is induced by passing a direct current (DC) through a coil, wrapped around an iron core (shoe).

Electron - the portion of an atom that carries a negative charge, the smallest charge of negative electricity. *See* Neutrons.

Equalization - the process of driving a liquid electrolyte lead-acid battery up to its highest natural voltage, in order to reconvert sulphated plate material back into active material.

F

Farad - the unit of capacitance.

Field windings - electrically magnetised coils used to create magnetic fields in alternators, generators, and electric motors.

Filament - a very fine piece of high-resistance wire that glows red (or white) hot when a current is passed through it.

Filter - a circuit that passes, or rejects, designated frequencies, signals or current.

Fluorescence - a light emitted when an inert gas is subject to electronic bombardment.

Frequency (Hz) - the number of times an alternating current (AC) goes through a complete cycle, in every second.

Fuse - a protective device designed to break a circuit by melting, if the current rises above a certain magnitude.

G

Gain - the amplification or magnification obtained within an electronic circuit.

Galvanic corrosion - a 'wasting' process that can occur when two or more dissimilar metals are placed in some proximity to each other, in an electrolyte - that is any solution capable of carrying an electric current, such as water.

Gassing - a by-product of a chemical reaction, such as the battery electrolyte giving off hydrogen and oxygen gases.

Generator - a machine for converting (or generating) rotary mechanical movement into electrical energy. Traditionally this was a dynamo, now superseded by the alternator.

Ground Fault Interrupter - a safety device that breaks a circuit, whenever a short to earth/ground occurs.

Ground - a common connection between an electric circuit and the earth, or some conducting body serving in place of the earth.

H

Heatsink - a (ribbed) mounting for electronic components, designed to dissipate heat to the atmosphere.

Henry (H) - a unit of inductance

Hertz (Hz) - the unit of frequency of an alternating current (AC). One hertz equals one cycle per second.

Hydrometer - a float-type pipette used to determine the state of charge of a battery by measuring the specific gravity of the electrolyte (ie the amount of sulphuric acid in the electrolyte).

Hysteresis - to introduce an electrical 'lead and lag' into the switching of a circuit. This is to be found in bilge pump float switches, where the switch is turned on at, say, 10° below the horizontal, and off at 15° below the horizontal. This 'pause' and staggering of the switching is to save the item constantly being switched on and off.

I

Impedance - opposition offered to the flow of alternating current (AC) in a circuit, measured in ohms.

Incandescent light - a light created by electrically heated filaments.

Inductance - a property of a conductor, or coil, that determines how much voltage will be induced (in it) by a change in the current passing through it. The unit of measurement is the Henry (H).

Induction motor - an AC motor.

Insulated return - a circuit in which both the outgoing and returning conductors are insulated.

Insulation - a material with extremely high electrical (or thermal) resistance.

Interference - undesired electrical signals.

Inverter - a device used to turn the applied signal upside down, or reverse its phase. Can also refer to power convertors. *See* Convertor.

Ion - a charged molecule. A particle that has lost or added electrons.

Integrated circuit - a complete circuit built on a chip of semi-conductor.

K

Kilocycle - 1,000 cycles per second; a unit for measuring the frequency of alternating current (AC).

Kilohertz (kHz) - one thousand Hertz.

Kilohm - one thousand ohms.

Kilowatt (kW) - one thousand watts.

L

Live - a circuit energized with electricity.

Load - any resistance or piece of electrical equipment that dissipates power when current flows through it.

Log - a device for measuring a craft's speed and distance run.

Lumens (per watt) - a measure of lighting output efficiency.

M

Machine sensed - a voltage regulator sensing voltage at the alternator, as opposed to at the battery.

Magnetic field - the area around a magnet, or a wire, carrying an electric current, in which magnetic forces are present. The iron-attracting, north and south poles draw opposite poles, and repel like poles.

Mains - the everyday word to describe a supply of domestic electric power - or 240V AC

Mega - 1,000,000, as in megawatt and megahertz.

Meter - any instrument that measures a quantity of current, resistance or voltage.

Micro - one-millionth of a unit of electricity, as uF or microfarad.

Microwaves - waves of between 30 cm and the infra-red region, extensively used for radar, or cooking.

Milli - one-thousandth of a unit of electricity - as millivolt or milliamp.

Mixer - a circuit unit that combines two frequencies.

Multi-meter - the 'equipment' for circuit testing. Also known as a VOM (volt-ohm meter), an AVO (amps-volts-ohms meter), a DMM (Digital multi-meter), or a DVM (Digital volt-meter).

N

Neutralization - a method of stabilizing an amplifier.

Neutrons - one of the three constituent parts of an atom, respectively neutrons, protons and electrons.

Nickel-cadmium battery (Ni-cad) - a battery with an alkaline electrolyte.

Noble metal - a metal high on the galvanic table. Noble metals are likely to form a cathode, in the case of galvanic corrosion, and are unlikely to corrode.

O

Ohm - the standard unit of measurement of resistance (or the resistance between two points on a conductor at a potential difference of one volt when a current of one ampere is flowing).

Ohmmeter - an instrument for measuring resistance - usually one function of a multi-meter.

Open circuit - a circuit with a broken or disconnected path (of electrical current).

Open-circuit voltage - the voltage of a battery that is not receiving, or delivering power.

Overcharging - forcing excessive current into a battery.

P

Parallel - term referred to equipment that is directly connected to a battery so that it receives the full battery voltage across it, as distinct from Series.

Parallel batteries - positive terminals are linked together, as are the negative terminals, to increase the system capacity, without increasing voltage.

Phase - the time relationship between two wave forms.

Points - metal pieces that 'make or break' the circuit, in various switching devices, such as pressure switches, solenoids, circuit breakers and ordinary switches.

Polarity - the distinction between positive and negative conductors in a DC system, and the opposite magnetic poles of an alternator, generator, or an electric motor.

Potential Difference - the value of voltage between two points of a circuit.

Potentiometer (POT) - a variable resistance used for adjusting some voltage regulators.

Power - the rate of doing work.

Power factor - the ratio of actual power to the apparent power.

Primary winding - the incoming side of a transformer.

Protons - *See* Neutrons.

R

Rectifier - A device for changing alternating current (AC) to direct current (DC). *See* Bridge rectifier & Diode.

Rectification - the process of converting an alternating current (AC) into a direct current (DC).

Relay - an electromechanical switch activated by a small current in an integral coil.

Residual magnetism - magnetism remaining in field winding cores, after the current has been cut off from the field windings.

Resistance - the 'opposition' in an appliance, or wire, to the flow of electric current, measured in ohms.

Resistor - a device of known resistance used in electronic circuits.

Reverse polarity - connecting a battery backwards, that is connecting the negative supply cable to the positive terminal, and the positive cable to the negative terminal.

Rheostat - an alternative name for a variable resistor - often fitted to large current circuits.

Rotor - the name given to the rotating field winding arrangement of an alternator.

S

Sacrificial anodes - anodes of a less noble metal (generally zinc or magnesium), fitted to protect below the water-line, metal components, from galvanic or electrolytic corrosion.

Screening - to reduce radiated and or induced interference.

Secondary winding - the output winding of a transformer.

Self-discharge - the gradual loss of capacity of a battery when standing idle.

Self-limiting - a built-in feature of some stator windings, limiting alternator output to a certain maximum, irrespective of speed.

Semi-conductors - a material that possesses a resistance, somewhere between that of conductors and insulators. By employing different types of semi-conductor materials, and joining/bonding them together, in various combinations, it is possible to form diodes, transistors, and other specialist components, in such a way that these devices control change, and alter the current flowing, in a variety of ways.

Separators - the material used to divide one battery plate from another.

Series - term referred to equipment that is connected to a battery, one after the other, so that they receive the same current.

Series batteries - where batteries are connected one after another, negative to positive. Batteries connect in series deliver greater voltage, but no greater capacity than a single battery.

Series-wound motors - a DC motor in which the field winding is connected in series with the armature.

Short-circuit - an unintentional, low resistance, alternative path for electric current. *See* Circuit.

Shunt - a special, low-resistance connection in a circuit that is used by an ammeter to sense the current flowing, in that circuit.

Shunt-wound motors - motors in which the field windings and armature are connected in parallel.

Sidebands (SB) - a band of frequencies on either or one side of a carrier frequency, in which radiation occurs due to modulation. In fact, this part of the transmitted wave carries the signal intelligence.

Silicon - a semi-conductor material.

Sine wave - the wave made by alternating current (AC) when voltage is charted against time.

Slip rings - insulated metal discs, on a rotor or armature shaft, through which current is fed, via brushes, to or from armature or rotor windings.

Slow blow fuse - a fuse with delayed action for use with motors having high-starting loads.

Solar panel - a collection of cells, usually sections of silicon, that convert sunlight/solar energy into electrical energy.

Solder - a low melting point metal - an amalgam of tin and lead.

Solenoid - an electrical coil with a hollow centre used as a magnet - a powerful relay.

Specific gravity - a measure of the density of the electrolyte solution in a battery, that is the strength of the acid and therefore the battery's state of charge.

Spike - a sudden high-voltage peak superimposed on a DC system.

Split charge relay - a relay used in multiple battery installations to isolate the batteries from each other, when they are not being charged. *See* Blocking Diodes.

Split charging - charging two or more batteries, from one charging source.

Stator - the stationary windings of an alternator within which the rotor spins.

Stray current corrosion - galvanic corrosion, amplified as a consequence of external current leakage present in the adjacent electrolyte.

Sulphation - the normal chemical transformation of battery plates when a battery discharges. If a battery is left in a discharged state, the sulphates crystalize and harden, causing a permanent loss of capacity.

Suppressor - a resistor put in series with the High Tension leads of a petrol engine ignition system to reduce ignition-radiated interference.

Surge current - the large current that is often drawn for a short period of time, when a piece of electrical equipment is initially turned on. *See* Slow blow fuse.

Surge protector - a special component that shorts out any high voltage spikes to ground. Used to protect voltage sensitive components. A Varistor is often used in this connection.

T

Thermistor - a resistor that changes in value, with changes in its temperature.

Thermocouple - a device containing two dissimilar metals, which generate a very small voltage when heated. They are used to open a solenoid on gas appliances - if the flame fails, the solenoid closes.

Tinning - a practical application to 'encourage' solder to adhere to a soldering iron, metals, wire ends, or fittings.

Transformer - an AC device with two or more coils used to magnetically couple one circuit to another. Depending on how the coils are wound, it can be used to lower, or raise voltage.

Transient voltage suppressor - *See* Surge Protector.

Trickle charge - a continuous, low current charge, usually applied to a battery.

U

Ultra high frequency (UHF) - Electromagnetic waves having frequencies between 300 and 3,000 megahertz (MHz).

Undercharging - the failure to bring a battery to full charge. This leads to sulphation and a permanent loss of capacity. *See* Sulphation.

V

Varistor - a resistor that changes its resistance value, depending upon the size of the applied voltage.

Volt (V) - the unit for electrical pressure, or the unit of electromotive force and potential difference. Officially, it is the difference in potential between two points on a conductor carrying a constant current of one ampere when the power dissipated is one watt.

Voltage drop - the loss in 'pressure' in wiring, switches, and connections due to unwanted resistance.

Voltage regulation - the process of controlling the output voltage of a device, irrespective of the input voltage, or the amount of current that the device has to supply to its load.

W

Watt (W) - a unit of electrical power - calculated by multiplying the current and voltage.

Wind generator - a generator (dynamo or alternator) driven by the wind.

Windings - coils in a motor or transformer.

ELECTRICAL EQUATIONS & FORMULAE

Ohm's Law: where
(a) Voltage (V) = Current (I - measured in amps) x Resistance (ohms),
(b) Current (I - or amps) = Voltage (V) ÷ Resistance (ohms), or
(c) Resistance (ohms) = Voltage (V) ÷ Current (I - or amps).

Power formula: where
(a) Power (watts) = Voltage (V) x Current (amps),
(b) Voltage (V) = Power (watts) ÷ Current (amps), or
(c) Current (amps) = Power (watts) ÷ Voltage (V).

Resistance, total of:
In a Series Circuit: Resistance = $R_1 + R_2 + R_3$...
In a Parallel Circuit: $1 \div R_T = 1 \div R_1 + 1 \div R_2 + 1 \div R_3 + ...$

Fuses, switches & relays: the minimum current rating should equal approximately 1.5 x the circuit current.

Electric Wire Colour Codes: all 240 AC mains equipment is fitted with wiring coded as follows:-
   live - brown; neutral - blue; earth - green/yellow.
If twin and earth cable is used for mains wiring, then the wire colours are:
   live - red; neutral - black; earth - uninsulated copper wire.
The following practice is commonly followed, for 12V and 24V DC, wiring installations   where:-
   + 12V/24V- red; 0V - black; ground - green.

Fuse wire - current capacity

| Diameter | | Standard | Current |
millimetres	inches	Wire Gauge	Capacity (amps)
0.213	0.0084	35	5
0.345	0.0136	29	10
0.510	0.020	25	15
0.610	0.024	23	20
0.815	0.033	21	30
1.02	0.040	19	38
1.43	0.056	17	65
1.83	0.072	15	77
2.03	0.080	14	100

Nobility Table

Potential	Material	Voltage
Least Noble	Magnesium alloy	-1.6
	Zinc	-1.10
	Galvanised iron	-1.05
	Aluminium	-0.75
	Mild steel	-0.70
	Cast iron	-0.65
	Lead	-0.55
	Brass*	-0.27/0.2
	Manganese bronze	-0.27
	Copper-Nickel	-0.25
	Silicon bronze	-0.18
	Monel*	-0.08/0.20
Most noble	Stainless steel*	-0.05/0.20

* The actual nobility depends upon the exact alloy composition of the metal.

To eliminate corrosion in sea-water it would be necessary to achieve a voltage difference of only 0.20 volts - so anodic protection is the answer.

Typical Cable/Current Requirements

Item	Current require-ment in amps (approx).	Conductor Specification in mm Single core	Twin Core	Cable Ref* Numbers	
Gauge lamps	6-8	14/0.30	2x14/0.30	PV2a76/1	PV2a 76/2
Interior lamps	9-12	21/0.30	2x21/0.30	PV2b76/1	PV2b 76/2
Larger lamps (such as search light)	17.5	28/0.30	2x28/0.30	PV376/1	PV3 76/2
Battery supply	27.5	44/0.30	2x44/0.30	PV3a76/1	PV3a 76/2
Dynamo	42	84/0.30	-	PV3b12/1	-
Alternator	60	120/0.30	-	PV3c12/1	-
Starter motors	135	266/0.30	-	PV336/1	-
	170	37/0.90	-	PV436/1	-
Electric winch	300	61/0.90	-	PV536/1	-

* These are Ripaults reference numbers.

USEFUL NAMES & ADDRESSES

General

Sell's Marine Market - The Boating Fact Finder, 55 High St, Epsom, Surrey, KT19 8DW.
British Marine Industries Federation, Boating Industry House, Vale Rd, Weybridge, Surrey, KT13 9NS.
British Waterways, Greycaine Rd, Watford, Herts, WD2 4JR.
Inland Waterways Association, 114 Regents Park Rd, London, NW1 8UQ.
Lloyds Register of Shipping, Lloyds Register House, 69 Oxford St, Southampton, Hants, SO1 1DL.
Royal Yachting Association (RYA), RYA House, Romsey Rd, Eastleigh, Hants, SO5 4YA.
National Rivers Authority, Thames Region, Kings Meadow House, Kings Meadow Rd, Reading, Berks, RG1 8BN.

A selection of specific companies:-

Specialist Retail Chandlers & Contractors

Taplins Marine*, 12 Shamrock Quay, Southampton, Hants, SO1 1QL.

Specialist Electrical Wholesale Chandlers

E.C. Smith & Sons Ltd, Unit H & J, Kingsway Industrial Estate, Kingsway, Luton, Beds, LU1 1LP.

Wholesale Chandlers & Equipment Suppliers

Sowester South Western Marine Factors Ltd,* PO Box 4, 43 Pottery Rd, Poole, Dorset, BH14 8RE.

Anodic Specialists

M.G. Duff Ltd, Unit 2 West, 68 Bognor Rd, Chichester, W. Sussex, PO19 2NZ.

Equipment & Instrument Manufacturers

Autopilots

Cetrek Ltd, 1 Factory Rd, Upton, Poole, Dorset, BH16 5SJ.
Nautech Ltd, Anchorage Park, Portsmouth, Hants, PO3 5TD.

Depth Sounders

Incastec Associates Ltd, 75/77 Christchurch Rd, Ringwood, Hants, BH24 1H.
Stowe Marine Equipment Ltd,* Parklands Business Park, Forest Rd, Denmead, Waterlooville, Hants, PO7 6XP.

Instrumentation

VDO Instruments Ltd, Holfordway, Holford, Birmingham, B6 7AX.

Logs

Stowe Marine Equipment Ltd,* Parklands Business Park, Forest Rd, Denmead, Waterlooville, Hants, PO7 6XP.
Seafarer International Ltd, Unit 2 Pipers Wood Industrial Park, Waterberry Drive, Waterlooville, Hants, PO9 1JL.

Position Locating Systems

Furuno (UK) Ltd, 187 Albert Quay, Aberdeen, AB1 2QA.
Navstar Ltd, Polytechnic Electronics Plc, Royal Oak Way, Daventry, Northants, NN11 5PJ.

Pumps, Electric - bilge & water

Munster Simms Engineering Ltd,* Old Belfast Rd, Bangor, Co. Down, BT19 1LT.

Radar

Raytheon Marine Sales & Service Co, The Pinnacles, Harlow, Essex, CM19 5AZ.
Kelvin Hughes Ltd, New North Rd, Hainault, Ilford, Essex, IG6 2UR.

Radio Telephone (VHF)

Kelvin Hughes Ltd, New North Rd, Hainault, Ilford, Essex, IG6 2UR.

Wind, Speed & Direction

Mariner Electronics Ltd, 1 Queensway, Stem Lane Industrial Estate, New Milton, Hants, BH25 5NN.
Stowe Marine Equipment Ltd,* Parklands Business Park, Forest Rd, Denmead, Waterlooville, Hants, PO7 6XP.

The companies marked with an asterisk have been very helpful and, in some instances have given a great deal of assurance.